GLENCOE

W9-BLA-886

The American Journey

Unit Resources

Nationalism and Sectionalism

The Jackson Era

Manifest Destiny

North and South

The Age of Reform

McGraw Hill Glencoe

Book Organization

Glencoe offers resources that accompany *The American Journey* to expand, enrich, review, and assess every lesson you teach and for every student you teach. Now Glencoe has organized its many resources for the way you teach.

How This Book Is Organized

Each Unit Resources book is divided into unit-based resources and chapter-based resources. A description of each of the many unit and chapter activities available to you in this book can be found on page v.

All unit-based resources appear at the beginning. Although you may choose to use the specific activities at any time during the course of unit study, Glencoe has placed these resources up front so that you can review your options.

Chapter-based resources follow the unit materials. These activities are directly tied to their chapter and/or section and should be used during the course of chapter study.

A Complete Answer Key

A complete answer key appears at the back of this book. This answer key includes answers for all activities in this book in the order in which the activities appear.

The McGraw·Hill Companies

 **Glencoe**

Copyright © by The McGraw-Hill Companies, Inc. All rights reserved. Permission is granted to reproduce the material contained herein on the condition that such materials be reproduced only for classroom use; be provided to students, teachers, and families without charge; and be used solely in conjunction with *The American Journey* program. Any other reproduction, for sale or other use, is expressly prohibited.

Send all inquiries to:
Glencoe/McGraw-Hill
8787 Orion Place
Columbus, OH 43240-4027

ISBN: 978-0-07-880599-8
MHID: 0-07-880599-6

Printed in the United States of America.

1 2 3 4 5 6 024 12 11 10 09 08

Table of Contents

North and South

The Age of Reform

To the Teacher

The American Journey Classroom Resources

Glencoe's Unit Resources are packed with activities for the varying needs of students. Included are the following activities:

Citizenship and Decision-Making Activities

These activities are designed to involve students in grassroots community projects. These service learning projects help students understand how history affects their own lives on a daily basis.

Economics and History Activities

These interdisciplinary activities give students an understanding of the impact of economics on history. Applied to current situations, students are familiarized with economic terms and principles.

Reading Skills Activities

These reinforcement activities correspond to the reading skill lessons presented in each unit opener of the student textbook. The activities allow students to gain additional practice at such reading skills as monitoring, making inferences, and summarizing.

American Literature Readings

These readings provide students with the opportunity to read literature by or about people who lived during different historical periods. Each selection is preceded by background information and a guided reading suggestion, and followed by comprehension and critical thinking questions.

Enrichment Activities

These activities introduce students to challenging content that is related to the information in the student textbook. Enrichment activities help students develop a broader and deeper understanding of history and the community.

Interpreting Political Cartoons

These activities provide students with the opportunity to explore history through serious fun called satire. Students will analyze the cartoons for various methods used in revealing satire such as caricature, symbolism, metaphor, irony, sarcasm, and stereotyping.

Content Vocabulary Activities

These review and reinforcement activities help students master unfamiliar content terms used in the student textbook. The worksheets provide visual and kinesthetic reinforcement of vocabulary words.

Academic Vocabulary Activities

Knowledge of academic terms can significantly boost students' comprehension of academic texts. These activities teach word parts, word relationships, grammar, and other lexical information about academic terms.

Primary Source Readings

These activities allow students to "see" history through the eyes of those who witnessed events and participated in cultural movements. Each selection is preceded by an introduction and a guided reading suggestion and is followed by questions that require students to analyze and interpret the material.

Writing Skills Activities

These activities help students develop and practice writing skills. Skills such as brainstorming, outlining, learning sentence structures, using sensory details, and writing essays are applied to historical concepts.

Social Studies Skills Activities

These activities allow students to practice their critical thinking and social studies skills. At times, activities extend information in the text and can also apply to real world situations. These activities will help students develop skills needed to understand new situations and content.

Differentiated Instruction Activities

These activities give you an opportunity to differentiate your instruction, addressing the different types of learners in your classroom. Teaching strategies address these differentiated learning styles: English Language Learners, Advanced Learners, Below Grade Level, Logical/Mathematical, Verbal/Linguistic, Visual/Spatial, Kinesthetic, Auditory/Musical, Interpersonal, and Intrapersonal.

Critical Thinking Skills Activities

Critical thinking skills are important to students because they provide the tools to live and work in an ever-changing world. These activities show students how to use information to make judgments, develop their own ideas, and apply what they have learned to new situations.

Geography and History Activities

These activities provide students with the opportunity to analyze and interpret historical maps. Students are required to practice using geography skills as an aid to understanding history.

Linking Past and Present Activities

These activities help students recognize the link between the past and the present and understand how the past relates to the present. For example, exploring the changes in information technology from the printing press to computerized desktop publishing will help students realize the past is a prologue to what is present in today's world.

Time Line Activities

These activities reinforce the dates of major events in world history and help students learn the chronological order of those events. Students also see how events occur concurrently in different parts of the world and/or are interrelated.

School-to-Home Connection Activities

These activities contain information and activities that students and their families/caregivers can do at home to reinforce an understanding of geography. They are intended to give parents easy materials to help their children with chapter lessons.

Reteaching Activities

These activities may be used for remediation or reinforcement. A variety of activities enable students to visualize the connections among facts in their textbook. Graphs, charts, lists, tables, and concept maps are among the many types of graphic organizers used.

Guided Reading Activities

These activities focus attention on key information and enable students to make appropriate connections among the facts they encounter in the student textbook. They also provide help for students who are having difficulty comprehending the textbook or who would benefit from a review of the material.

Nationalism and Sectionalism

Name_____ Date_____ Class_____

Unit

Citizenship and Decision-Making Activity
Nationalism and Sectionalism

Connecting With Native Americans

> ## Why It Matters
> Education, personality, religion, social status, and shared experiences each have an influence on a cultural group. Shared experiences may be the most influential. Gaining an understanding of the past events that helped shape a culture can help us understand that culture today.

Background

In the late 1700s, the U.S. government recognized the Cherokee people as a separate nation. They created their own written constitution. Further protection was granted by the Supreme Court through the *Cherokee Nation* v. *Georgia* and *Worcester* v. *Georgia* legal cases. However, the American settlers and President Jackson had a strong desire for the Cherokee land. Therefore, all treaties were essentially ignored by the 1830s.

In 1838 President Jackson authorized the army to evacuate the Cherokee people from northern Georgia by force because they would not comply with the Indian Removal Act of 1830. The long walk from Georgia to Oklahoma was devastating; many Cherokee died from exposure and fatigue. That route became known as the Trail of Tears. Some Cherokee escaped along the trail and hid in the woods. Later, these escapees banded together to form part of the Eastern Band of Cherokee. Today the Cherokee live primarily on reservations in North Carolina and Oklahoma.

Of course, the life of the Cherokee has changed significantly since the 1800s. However, the Cherokee people have been able to preserve many of their traditions. Today, their typical occupations range from farming to business management. The tourism industry provides a major source of income. Hospitality is a distinguishing Cherokee characteristic.

Citizenship and Decision-Making Activity (continued)

Questions to Consider

Directions: Answer the questions below on a separate sheet of paper.

1. **Analyzing** How do you think being removed from their native lands affected Cherokee traditions and ways of life?

2. **Explaining** What happened to the Cherokee who were able to escape from the army and avoid being moved to Oklahoma?

Your Task

Create a multimedia presentation about a specific group of Native Americans and their important issues.

How to Do It

Work in small groups, and follow the steps below:

1. Use resources at the library or on the Internet to locate a list of Native American groups within the United States. Choose one of the groups to research. Try to locate information about daily life on the reservation, education, income, historical traditions, and current customs for the group you chose.

2. Assign a different task to each member of your group. Tasks could include writing paragraphs about the daily life of your Native American group, creating artwork, putting together the overall presentation, and working the slide projector or computer during the presentation.

3. Present your material to another group, and solicit feedback on the quality of your presentation. In turn, provide feedback to the other group.

4. Present your multimedia program to the entire class.

Follow-Up Activity

Write a poem or a song that reflects the customs or traditions of the Native American group you researched. Share your poems or songs as a class.

> **Did You Know?**
>
> Today the Eastern Band of the Cherokee in North Carolina has more than 13,000 enrolled members. What is now their reservation land was originally purchased by a white man named Will Thomas, a colonel for the South during the Civil War. Many Cherokee fought against the North under Thomas. In the late 1800s, the land Thomas purchased was given to the Cherokee people.

Self-Assessment Checklist

Assess your presentation using the checklist below:

☐ We chose a Native American group.

☐ We found information on the group's daily life, education, income, etc.

☐ We prepared a presentation with slides or on a computer.

☐ Our presentation had artwork and written information on our Native American group.

☐ We obtained feedback from other class members on our presentation.

Economics and History Activity

Nationalism and Sectionalism

The National Bank

Before the United States had a national bank, state banks printed bank notes, or paper money. The banks promised to exchange the notes for gold or silver upon demand of the holder. This promise was intended to support the value of paper money. However, the banks often did not have enough gold and silver on hand to back up the notes. Thus, people did not trust the paper money, so the notes were seldom worth the amount printed on them.

To solve this problem, Congress established the Second Bank of the United States in 1816. The bank issued national paper money and kept a large supply of gold and silver to back the notes. It also set limits on the amount of notes that state banks could issue. In 1832 President Andrew Jackson vetoed the bank's request to renew its charter. Like many Americans at that time, Jackson believed the bank had too much power.

Without regulation from a central bank, the country experienced wide fluctuations in its money supply, or total amount of money in circulation. Sometimes state banks printed many paper notes and made many loans. Other times they did the opposite. These changes in the money supply resulted in wide swings in economic activity.

In 1913 Congress created today's national bank: the Federal Reserve System, or the Fed. The Fed prints the nation's paper money and makes rules that local banks must follow. The Fed's main purpose is to help stabilize economic activity. It accomplishes this purpose by influencing the money supply.

The Fed requires banks to hold a certain percentage of their total deposits in reserve. Banks may lend the rest of their deposits to earn interest on the loans. The more money banks can lend, the larger the money supply is. The table below shows how the Fed can increase or decrease the money supply by changing the reserve requirement. In this way, the Fed can speed up or slow down economic activity.

Reserve Requirement and the Money Supply			
Bank Deposits	**Percentage of Reserve Requirement**	**Dollar Amount of Reserve**	**Dollar Amount Bank May Loan**
$100,000	5%	$5,000	$95,000
$100,000	10%	$10,000	$90,000
$100,000	12%	$12,000	$88,000
$100,000	15%	Y	Z

Economics and History Activity (continued)

✓ Applying Economics to History

Directions: Use the information on the previous page to answer the following questions in the spaces provided.

1. **Analyzing** In the early 1800s, what gave state bank notes their value?

_____

2. **Explaining** Why were state bank notes seldom worth the value printed on them?

_____

_____

3. **Determining Cause and Effect** How did Andrew Jackson's veto of the National Bank affect the economy?

_____

_____

4. **Explaining** How does the Fed help stabilize economic activity today?

_____

5. **Calculating** In the table, what number should replace Y? What number should replace Z?

_____

GOING FURTHER ▶ ▶▶▶

- Changing the reserve requirement is only one of the ways that the Fed can influence the money supply. The Fed has two other important tools: open market operations and the discount rate. Conduct research to learn more about these tools. Then use what you learn to complete the table below. For each Fed action, indicate whether the action increases or decreases the money supply.

Tool	Fed Action	Money Supply (increases or decreases)
Reserve Requirement	Lower	
	Raise	
Open Market Operations	Buy bonds	
	Sell bonds	
Discount Rate	Lower	
	Raise	

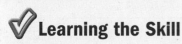

Reading Skills Activity

Nationalism and Sectionalism

Making Inferences

✓ Learning the Skill

Can you imagine how large a textbook would be if the author had to define every word and idea for you? Authors rely on a reader's ability to make inferences because all of the details cannot always be provided. You make inferences while you are reading by drawing conclusions about information that is implied—or not directly stated. You use details in the text and from your own experience to make inferences. That is what is meant by the phrase "reading between the lines."

Use the following guidelines to make inferences as you read:

- Decide what general topic is being presented.
- Review what you already know about the topic.
- Read carefully for stated facts and ideas.
- Use logic and common sense to form a conclusion about the topic.

✓ Practicing the Skill

Directions: Read the passage below, and then answer the questions that follow.

> Joseph Smith founded the Church of Jesus Christ of Latter-day Saints in 1830 in New York State. He had visions that led him to launch a new Christian church. He hoped to use these visions to build an ideal society. But the controversial beliefs of Smith and his followers, called Mormons, aroused a great deal of suspicion and animosity.
>
> Smith believed that property should be held in common. He also supported polygamy, the idea that a man could have more than one wife. This angered many people and Mormons eventually gave up this practice.
>
> Smith formed a community in New York, but unsympathetic neighbors disapproved of the Mormons' religion. They forced the Mormons to move on. From New York, the Mormons went to Ohio, then to Missouri, and then to Illinois.
>
> In 1844 a mob in Illinois killed Smith, and Brigham Young took over as head of the Mormons. Young decided the Mormons should move again, this time near the Great Salt Lake in present-day Utah. Although part of Mexico at that time, no Mexicans had settled in the region because of its harsh terrain.

1. **Identifying** What topic is the author describing?

_____

2. **Describing** What were some controversial Mormon beliefs and practices?

_____

Copyright © Glencoe/McGraw-Hill, a division of The McGraw-Hill Companies, Inc.

Reading Skills Activity (continued)

3. **Making Inferences** Using the text and what you already know, what can you infer about the reason Joseph Smith was killed?

_____

_____

✓Applying the Skill

Directions: Read the passage below. Then answer the questions that follow on a separate piece of paper.

> Mormons began moving to the Great Salt Lake area in 1846. About 12,000 Mormons made the journey. This was the largest single migration in American history. They set up their communities in the middle of the desert. Mormons named the area Deseret.
>
> With hard work and determination, the Mormons made Deseret grow. They planned their towns carefully. They built irrigation canals to water their farms and built industries so they could be self-sufficient. Mormon merchants sold supplies to the forty-niners who passed through Utah on their way to the gold fields of California.
>
> When the Mexican War ended in 1848, the Salt Lake area became part of the United States. In 1850 Congress established the Utah Territory. President Millard Fillmore made Brigham Young its governor.
>
> Utah was not easily incorporated into the United States. The Mormons often had conflicts with federal officials. In 1857 and 1858, war almost broke out between the Mormons and the United States Army. Utah did not become a state until 1896.

1. **Finding the Main Idea** What is the main idea of this passage?

2. **Identifying** What was Deseret?

3. **Contrasting** How did the Mormon migration west differ from that of the forty-niners who were bound for California?

4. **Making Inferences** What can you infer about the living conditions the Mormons found in the Great Salt Lake area?

5. **Sequencing** Which came first—the Mormon migration or the migration of forty-niners? How do you know?

6. **Making Inferences** Why do you think Utah was not easily incorporated into the United States? Explain your answer.

Copyright © Glencoe/McGraw-Hill, a division of The McGraw-Hill Companies, Inc.

Unit

American Literature Reading
Nationalism and Sectionalism

Black Hawk

About the Selection

Black Hawk was a Sauk warrior. His Native American nation was defeated by white settlers in Illinois in the Black Hawk War in 1832. White leaders were notably cruel and vicious during the war, even attacking the Native Americans as they attempted to surrender. Black Hawk was captured with his son and put on display as trophies of war. When he was released, he returned to his family and wrote his autobiography.

Guided Reading

As you read the autobiography, make a note of the relationships between the whites and Native Americans.

 Reader's Dictionary

provision: a stock of necessary supplies, especially food

apprehended: understood

endeavored: attempted

expired: died

lamenting: grieving, mourning

countenance: facial expression

avenge: to take revenge

The Life of Black Hawk

by Black Hawk (Ma-Ka-Tai-Me-She-Kia-Kiak), 1833

The war chief at Peoria is a very good man; he always speaks the truth, and treats our people well. He sent for me one day, and told me that he was nearly out of **provision,** and wished me to send my young men out to hunt, to supply his fort. I promised to do so; and immediately returned to my camp, and told my young men the wishes and wants of the war chief. They readily agreed to go and hunt for our friend; and soon returned with about twenty deer. They carried them to the fort, laid them down at the gate, and returned to our camp. A few days afterwards, I went again to the fort to see if they wanted more meat. The chief gave me some powder and lead, and said he wished me to send my hunters out again. When I returned to my camp, and told my young men that the chief wanted more meat, Má-ta-táh, one of my principal braves, said he would take a party and go across the Illinois, about one day's travel, where game was plenty, and make a good hunt for our friend, the war chief. He took eight hunters with him. . . . They had traveled about half the day in the prairie, when they discovered

American Literature Reading (continued)

The Life of Black Hawk (continued)

a party of white men coming towards them with a drove of cattle. Our hunters **apprehended** no danger, or they would have kept out of the way of the whites. . . . As soon as the whites saw our party, some of them put off at full speed, and came up to our hunters. Má-ta-táh gave up his gun to them, and **endeavored** to explain to them that he was friendly, and was hunting for the war chief. They were not satisfied with this, but fired at and wounded him. . . . He found that he would be murdered, and sprung at the nearest man to him, seized his gun, and shot him from his horse. He then fell, covered with blood from his wounds, and almost instantly **expired**!

The other hunters, being in the rear of Má-ta-táh, seeing that the whites had killed him, endeavored to make their escape. They were pursued, and nearly all the party *murdered!* My youngest brother brought me the news in the night, he having been with the hunters, and got but slightly wounded. . . . The remainder of the night was spent in **lamenting** for the death of our friends. At day-light, I blacked my face, and started to the fort to see the war chief. I met him at the gate, and told him what had happened. His **countenance** changed; I could see sorrow depicted in it for the death of my people. He tried to persuade me that I was mistaken, as he 'could not believe that the whites would act so cruelly.' But when I convinced him, he told me that those "cowards who had murdered my people should be punished." I told him that my people would have revenge—that they would not trouble any of his people of the fort, as we did not blame him or any of his soldiers—but that a party of my braves would go towards the Wabash to **avenge** the death of their friends and relations. The next day I took a party of hunters and killed several deer, and left them at the fort gate as I passed.

Source: *The First West: Writing From the American Frontier, 1776–1860.* Ed. by Edward Watts and David Rachels. Oxford University Press. 2002.

Literary Response and Analysis

Directions: Answer the following questions on a separate sheet of paper.

1. **Describing** What kind of relationship did the writer have with the white leader of the fort at Peoria?

2. **Identifying** Why did Má-ta-táh and other braves make a journey across the prairie?

3. **Critical Thinking** How did the writer feel about white people?

Copyright © Glencoe/McGraw-Hill, a division of The McGraw-Hill Companies, Inc.

Name_____ Date_____ Class_____

Enrichment Activity

Nationalism and Sectionalism

Stories of Escape on the Underground Railroad

The Underground Railroad was not really a railroad, and the people on this "railroad" did not travel underground. Instead, the Underground Railroad was a secret network of escape routes that were used by enslaved people to get from the South to the North and on to freedom. Like a true railroad, stops along the Underground Railroad were called "stations" or "depots," and the people who guided the runaways were called "conductors." Much of what we know about the Underground Railroad comes from the stories that were related to the conductors and "stationmasters" along these routes.

The Stories of William Still

Born in New Jersey in 1821, William Still was the youngest of 18 children. Both of his parents had formerly been enslaved. William's father, Levin, bought his freedom. His mother, Sidney, escaped from slavery. She was forced to leave two of her children behind when she escaped.

As a child, William worked on his family's farm and learned to read and write. As a young adult, he made his way to Philadelphia and found work with the Pennsylvania Society for the Abolition of Slavery. In Philadelphia, William was able to provide runaways with a place to rest as they made their way to Canada.

William's work as a stationmaster on the Underground Railroad allowed him to help many people, including his own brother. William talked with the runaways who stayed with him and listened to their stories of courage. He kept careful records of their stories and later published them in a book entitled *The Underground Railroad*.

One of the stories William collected was of his own mother and his brother Peter. In his book, William describes the night his mother left his brother to head north:

> "On the night she started she went to the bed where they were sleeping, kissed them, and, consigning them into the hands of God, bade her mother good-bye, and with her two little girls wended her way again to Burlington County, New Jersey, but to a different neighborhood from that where she had been seized. She changed her name to Charity, and succeeded in again joining her husband, but, alas, with the heart-breaking thought that she had been compelled to leave her two little boys in slavery and one of the little girls on the road for the father to go back after. Thus she began life in freedom anew.
>
> Levin and Peter, eight and six years of age respectively, were now left at the mercy of the enraged owner, and were soon hurried off to a Southern market and

Enrichment Activity (continued)

(continued)

sold, while their mother, for whom they were daily weeping, was they knew not where. They were too young to know that they were slaves, or to understand the nature of the afflicting separation. Sixteen years before Peter's return, his older brother (Levin) died a slave in the State of Alabama, and was buried by his surviving brother, Peter.

No idea other than that they had been "kidnapped" from their mother ever entered their minds; nor had they any knowledge of the State from whence they supposed they had been taken, the last names of their mother and father, or where they were born. On the other hand, the mother was aware that the safety of herself and her rescued children depended on keeping the whole transaction a strict family secret. During the forty years of separation, except two or three Quaker friends, . . . it is doubtful whether any other individuals were let into the secret of her slave life. And when the account given of Peter's return, etc., was published in 1850, it led some of the family to apprehend [fear] serious danger from the partial revelation of the early condition of the mother, especially as it was about the time that the Fugitive Slave law was passed."

Investigating Underground Railroad Stories

Use the Internet to find other stories of escape on the Underground Railroad. Choose a story that you find particularly compelling and present it to the class in multimedia format. Include a map showing the route of escape, as well as pictures that relate to the story. For added effect, include music from the period in your presentation. Be sure to document all of your sources.

Self-Assessment Checklist

Assess your presentation using the checklist below:

☐ I chose a story of escape on the Underground Railroad.

☐ I developed an accurate and interesting presentation.

☐ I accurately mapped the escape route described in the story.

☐ I enhanced my presentation with relevant pictures and music.

☐ I used appropriate pacing and tone of voice in my presentation.

☐ I documented all of my sources.

Interpreting Political Cartoons

Nationalism and Sectionalism

Disputes Over Slavery

The cartoon below, which was published in 1835, illustrates the growing disputes over the issue of slavery. The main figure, a Southern judge, sentences a white abolitionist to death by hanging.

Directions: Study the cartoon below, and then answer the questions that follow.

Library of Congress, Prints & Photographs Division, LC-USZ62-92284

1. **Analyzing Visuals** Why is the judge pictured sitting on bales of cotton and tobacco?

   _____

   _____

2. **Analyzing Visuals** Why does the judge have a foot on the Constitution?

   _____

   _____

Interpreting Political Cartoons (continued)

3. **Making Connections** Why is the judge shown with a donkey's ears and carrying a whip?

_____

_____

Critical Thinking

4. **Making Inferences** Why would Southerners not want abolitionists to be active in the South?

_____

_____

_____

5. **Analyzing Information** Why is the cartoon titled "Southern Ideas of Liberty"?

_____

_____

_____

6. **Drawing Conclusions** Is this cartoon more sympathetic to the South or to abolitionists? Explain.

_____

_____

_____

Chapter Resources

The Jackson Era

Content Vocabulary Activity

The Jackson Era

Fill in the Blanks **DIRECTIONS** Select a term from the box below to complete each of the sentences that follow.

majority	nominating convention	relocate
plurality	tariff	guerrilla tactics
spoils system	nullify	veto
caucus	secede	depression
laissez-faire		

1. In the 1830s, as conflicts between white settlers and Native Americans grew, many settlers wanted to _____ Native Americans to other parts of the country.

2. In the presidential election of 1824, Andrew Jackson won the largest single share, or _____ , of the votes.

3. In 1832 Andrew Jackson used his power to _____ the bill that would renew the Bank of the United States' charter.

4. The Seminole used _____ against the United States, attacking them by surprise and then retreating back into the forests and swamps.

5. President Jackson practiced the _____ and replaced government employees with his supporters while he was in office.

6. A _____ on imported European goods made them more expensive to purchase in America.

7. The Panic of 1837 was the beginning of a(n) _____ in which business activity and employment fell to a very low level.

8. In 1832 South Carolina threatened to _____ from the Union because the state did not agree with the fees placed on imported goods.

9. Because no one candidate received the _____ of the electoral votes in the election of 1824, Andrew Jackson was declared the winner.

Content Vocabulary Activity (continued)

10. During Andrew Jackson's presidency, the unpopular

   _____ system of members of Congress choosing
   candidates ended.

11. President Van Buren supported the principle of _____,
   which included limited government interference in the nation's
   economy.

12. A(n) _____ allowed delegates from the states to
   choose the party's presidential candidate.

13. John C. Calhoun of South Carolina wanted to _____,
   or cancel, the federal law that imposed a fee on all imported goods.

Academic Vocabulary Activity

The Jackson Era

Academic Words in This Chapter

select	federal	institution
participate	survive	symbol

A. Word Meaning Activity: Categorizing Words

Directions: *Synonyms* are words with similar meanings. Read the underlined words below, as well as the four words or phrases next to them. Three of the words or phrases are similar in meaning to the underlined word. Circle the word or phrase that is *not similar* to the underlined word.

1. select: choose, discard, appoint, designate

2. participate: experience, take part in, sit out, join

3. federal: regional, countrywide, central, national

4. survive: live through, perish, endure, persist

5. institution: corporation, foundation, establishment, store

6. symbol: emblem, currency, design, logo

B. Word Usage Activity: Using Academic Words

Directions: Use a form of the academic words at the top of this page to replace the underlined common words in the lines below.

1. The soldiers who <u>stayed alive</u> called for more troops to help protect the

   settlements. _____

2. Political parties created <u>objects</u> that represent their groups to the American

   people. _____

3. Each representative wrote his <u>nomination</u> for office on the ballot.

   _____

4. The Bank of the United States became a powerful <u>organization</u> in the

   government. _____

5. The candidates each had different ideas about the role of the <u>central</u>

   government. _____

19

Academic Vocabulary Activity (continued)

C. Word Family Activity: Completing a Word Chart

Directions: A *noun* is a word that names a person, a place, a thing, or an idea. Examples include *president, Chicago, army,* and *slavery*. A *verb* is a word that is used to describe an action, an experience, or a state of being. Examples include *govern, attempt,* and *seem*. An *adjective* is a word used to describe a noun. Examples include *interesting, numeric,* and *comical*. Some words have more than one form. Place a check mark (√) in the appropriate column.

Words	Noun	Verb	Adjective
1. select			
2. selection			
3. participating			
4. participation			
5. participate			
6. federal			
7. federation			
8. survive			
9. surviving			
10. survivor			
11. institution			
12. institutionalize			
13. symbol			
14. symbolize			
15. symbolic			

Primary Source Readings

The Jackson Era

The Trail of Tears

Interpreting the Source

In 1835 the federal government persuaded a few Cherokee to sign a treaty giving up their people's land. Yet most of the Cherokee refused to honor the treaty. They wrote a protest letter to the government and people of the United States, pleading for understanding. It did not soften the resolve of President Jackson or the area's white settlers. In 1838 federal troops threatened force if the Cherokee did not leave. The Cherokee knew that fighting would only lead to their doom. Filled with sadness and anger, their leaders yielded, and the long march to the West began. John Burnett was a soldier assigned to accompany the Cherokee on what became known as the Trail of Tears. The following is an excerpt from his memoirs.

Guided Reading

As you read, evaluate the author's point of view on the removal of the Cherokee and how it affects this account.

Reader's Dictionary

bayonet: a steel blade attached to the end of a rifle

solemnity: seriousness

fateful: extremely unfortunate results

pneumonia: a lung disease

The Cherokee Removal

On . . . hunting trips I met and became acquainted with many of the Cherokee Indians, hunting with them by day and sleeping around their camp fires by night. I learned to speak their language, and they taught me the arts of trailing and building traps and snares. . . .

The removal of the Cherokee Indians from their life long homes in the year of 1838 found me a young man in the prime of life and a private soldier in the American Army. . . . I saw the helpless Cherokees arrested and dragged from their homes, and driven at the **bayonet** point into the stockades. And In the chill of a drizzling rain on an October morning I saw them loaded like cattle or sheep into six hundred and forty-five wagons and started toward the west.

One can never forget the sadness and **solemnity** of that morning. . . . Many of these helpless people did not have blankets and many of them had been driven from home barefooted.

On the morning of November the 17th we encountered a terrific sleet and snow storm with freezing temperatures and from that day until we reached the

Primary Source Readings (continued)

The Cherokee Removal (continued)

end of the **fateful** journey on March the 26th 1839, the sufferings of the Cherokees were awful. The trail of the exiles was a trail of death. They had to sleep in the wagons and on the ground without fire. And I have known as many as twenty-two of them to die in one night of **pneumonia** due to ill treatment, cold, and exposure. . . .

    Future generations will . . . condemn the [removal of the Cherokee]. . . .

Source: John G. Burnett. "The Cherokee Removal Through the Eyes of a Private Soldier," in *The Removal of the Cherokee.* Cherokee, N.C.: Museum of the Cherokee Indian, Publication 305.

DBQ Document-Based Questions

Directions: Answer the questions below in the spaces provided.

1. **Identifying** What events in John Burnett's life might have caused him to feel the way he does about the Cherokee?

   _____

   _____

2. **Illustrating** What imagery does Burnett use to describe his fellow soldiers' treatment of the Cherokee?

   _____

   _____

3. **Specifying** What does Burnett blame for the deaths of so many Cherokee on the trail?

   _____

   _____

4. **Explaining** Burnett is convinced that "future generations will condemn" the forced removal of the Cherokee. Was he correct?

   _____

   _____

5. **Formulating Questions** What question would you ask the writer of this passage?

   _____

Writing Skills Activity

The Jackson Era

Employing Descriptive Strategies

 Learning the Skill

Which of the following descriptions of Andrew Jackson's background grabs your attention?

> "Andrew Jackson was born in a log cabin and became president of the United States."
>
> "Andrew Jackson, a true American success story, grew up the son of Scotch-Irish immigrants in a hand-hewn log cabin that had a mixture of clay and straw stuffed between the logs. After a humble beginning, he become the president of the United States and represented the average American citizen at the highest level of government."

When writing a narrative or short story, description plays a major role in telling the story and bringing events to life for the reader. Descriptions give a verbal picture of characters and events, including the settings in which the events take place.

Follow these steps in using description effectively in your writing:

- Determine which descriptive details will enhance your story (such as what the characters look like, what the physical setting is like, and what took place before the story began).
- Determine how you will present this information. Will you simply describe the details? Will you illustrate a person's attitudes or temperament through dialogue? How will you set up the action to move the story along?
- Be creative in your choice of language. Saying someone is fatigued or worn out conveys a more vivid picture than saying someone is tired.

 Practicing the Skill

Directions: Find the word in Column 2 that presents a more descriptive picture of the word in Column 1. Write the letter of that word next to the number in Column 1.

Column 1

_____ **1.** dry

_____ **2.** eager

_____ **3.** walked

_____ **4.** happy

_____ **5.** ran

Column 2

A. joyful

B. scampered

C. parched

D. trudged

E. impatient

Writing Skills Activity (continued)

✓ Applying the Skill

Directions: Imagine you are a part of the crowd attending the White House reception after President Jackson's Inaugural Address. Write a short description of what it was like to be there.

_____

_____

_____

_____

_____

_____

_____

_____

_____

_____

_____

_____

_____

_____

_____

_____

_____

_____

_____

Self-Assessment Checklist

Assess your paragraph using the checklist below:

☐ I described the place and people of the reception.

☐ I used descriptive details to enhance the story.

☐ I chose creative words in place of more ordinary words.

☐ I checked my writing for correct spelling, grammar, and punctuation.

Social Studies Skills Activity

The Jackson Era

Sequencing of Events

 ## Learning the Skill

Sequencing is placing facts in the logical order in which they occurred. This means that you can organize large quantities of information in an easily understandable order. Some examples of the different ways to sequence events are descriptive text, time lines, and graphs.

To recognize and sequence events, follow these steps:

- Look for dates or clue words that describe chronological order, such as *in 2007, in the late 1900s, first, then,* and so on.
- Look for ways to identify relationships among events.
- Read the titles and facts on time lines to follow the order of events.
- Analyze the axis dates in graphs to determine the span of years covered.

 ## Practicing the Skill

Directions: Read the following paragraph about events related to Andrew Jackson's closing of the Bank of the United States. Then number the events that follow in sequential order in which they occurred.

> In 1832 Daniel Webster and Henry Clay planned to block Andrew Jackson's reelection. They persuaded Nicolas Biddle, president of the Bank of the United States, a man Jackson disliked, to apply for renewal of the charter before it was ready to expire. Webster and Clay thought Jackson's veto of the bank charter would lead to his defeat. The plan failed when many who felt the Bank was unconstitutional supported Jackson in his veto of the charter's bill. As it turned out, Jackson was reelected. Jackson then decided to take action against the Bank. He ordered government deposits withdrawn from the Bank. The funds were distributed among the smaller state banks. Finally, after Jackson refused to sign a new charter, the Bank closed in 1836.

Source: www.britannica.com/ebc/article-3619

_____ Jackson refuses to sign a new Bank charter in 1836 and it closes.

_____ Jackson's veto is supported, resulting in his reelection.

_____ Clay and Webster persuade Biddle to apply for a new Bank charter.

_____ Jackson rejects the charter application by veto.

_____ Jackson withdraws all government deposits from the Bank.

Social Studies Skills Activity (continued)

✓ Applying the Skill

Directions: A time line provides an organized look at a sequence of events. In the space provided below, create a time line that shows the major events of your life from birth to present.

Title:_____

Self-Assessment Checklist

Assess your sequence of events time line using the checklist below:

☐ I created a sequence of events time line to show the major events of my life.

☐ I made sure the information was in logical order and made sense.

☐ I presented my sequence of events time line clearly to classmates.

☐ I explained what I learned about using a sequence of events time line.

☐ With permission, I displayed my sequence of events time line.

Differentiated Instruction Activity

The Jackson Era

The Trail of Tears

In 1838 the U.S. government forced the Cherokee from their homeland in the southeastern United States to the Indian Territory in what is now Oklahoma. Their journey west became known as the Trail of Tears. The Cherokee were divided into 16 detachments of about 1,000 each. Three detachments of Cherokee, totaling about 2,800 persons, traveled by river to Indian Territory. The rest went overland on existing roads, taking roughly 10 individual routes. The Northern Route was most commonly used; other detachments (notably those led by John Benge and John Bell) followed more southern routes. Others followed slight variations.

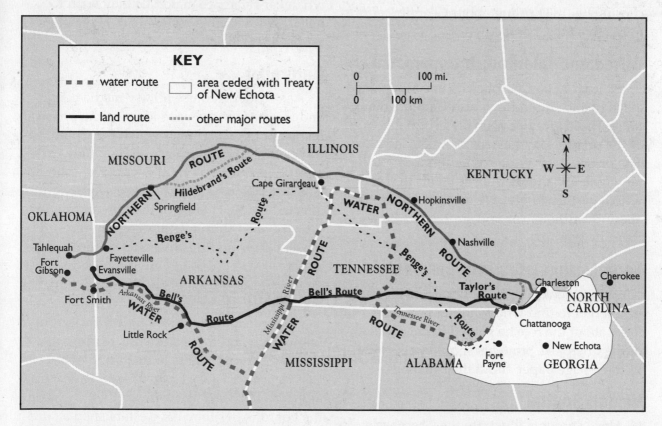

Directions: Use the information from the map and your textbook to answer the following questions on a separate sheet of paper.

1. **Describing** Write a paragraph that traces the path of the Northern Route.

2. **Calculating** Determine the length in miles of the Water Route, the Northern Route, Benge's Route, and Bell's Route, as shown on the map. Estimate how long it might have taken to complete each route. Speculate on how these distances and time frames might have impacted the movement of the Cherokee on their journey.

Differentiated Instruction Activity (continued)

Teaching Strategies for Different Learning Styles

The following activities are ways the basic lesson can be modified to accommodate students' different learning styles.

English Language Learner (ELL)

Have students identify all of the towns, states, and rivers on the map. Also ask them to identify in what states Cherokee Territory existed *before* their travels on the Trail of Tears.

Gifted and Talented

Write a letter from Chief Justice John Marshall to President Andrew Jackson concerning his 1832 ruling about Georgia's efforts to remove the Cherokee.

Gifted and Talented; Interpersonal

At least 1,000 Cherokee escaped the forced eviction and hid in the North Carolina mountains. These individuals have become the root of the present-day Eastern Band of Cherokee. The present-day Western Band is located largely in Oklahoma. Ask students to work with a partner to prepare oral presentations about the differences and similarities between these two groups.

Verbal/Linguistic; Intrapersonal

Ask students to use the library media center or Internet to find who John Ross was and learn about the role he played in the removal of the Cherokee. Students should write a two- to three-page paper about their findings.

Visual/Spatial

Have students illustrate the Cherokee's journey along the Trail of Tears. Urge them to make their illustrations historically accurate (e.g., clothing styles, types of wagons, etc.) based on research.

Kinesthetic; Interpersonal

Have students work with a partner to write a dialogue that might have occurred in one of the following situations: two Cherokee discuss the possibility of escaping into the Smoky Mountains rather than making the journey to Indian Territory; two white residents of Cape Girardeau, Missouri, discuss the approaching Cherokee on their trek west; a Cherokee leader who agreed to cede the tribal territory in exchange for money and land in Indian Territory justifies his decision to a skeptical Cherokee. Students may consult whatever reference materials they wish to help them with this assignment. Have pairs act out their dialogues to the class.

Naturalist

Ask students to use library media center and Internet resources to identify the physical features of the land over which the Cherokee traveled on their journey and how they used natural resources along the way. They should also describe how the Cherokee's journey was affected by the climate of the different regions they traveled through. Students should present their findings in a two- to three-page paper.

Below Grade Learners

Use anticipation guides to test background knowledge and focus students' reading in a chapter. Have students brainstorm: *What problems were faced by the Cherokee upon their arrival in Indian Territory?* Write down their ideas on the board. After they have established a sufficient list, have students select the four or five problems they think are the most important. In complete sentences, students should write the ideas on a piece of paper, explaining why they think these were significant problems. As they read the chapter and conduct independent research, have them revisit the sentences and correct any misconceptions.

Critical Thinking Skills Activity

The Jackson Era

Identifying the Main Idea

Learning the Skill

Identifying the main idea helps you understand historical concepts and how historical events unfold. To identify the main idea in a reading, identify the purpose of the passage and look for the ways important details relate to one another.

Practicing the Skill

Directions: Read the excerpts, and then answer the questions that follow.

From the annual message to Congress of President Andrew Jackson, 1830:

". . . Humanity has often wept over the fate of the aborigines [Native Americans] in this country, and the Philanthropy [effort to help] has been long busily employed in the devising means to avert [turn away from] it . . . but one by one have many powerful tribes disappeared from the earth. . . . Nor is there anything in this which . . . is to be regretted. Philanthropy could not wish to see this continent restored to the condition in which it was found by our forefathers. What good man would prefer a country covered with forests and ranged by a few thousand savages to our expensive Republic, studded with cities, towns, and prosperous farms, embellished [made better] with all the improvements which . . . industry executes [carries out]. . . . "

From a message written by Senator Frelinghuysen of New Jersey, 1830:

". . . His lands are constantly coveted [wanted by others]; millions after millions [of acres] are ceded [given over]. The Indian . . . complains . . . but suffers on; and now he finds that his neighbors, whom his kindness had nourished, has spread an adverse title [bad claim] over the last remains of his patrimony [inheritance]. . . . Do the obligations of justice change with the color of the skin? Is it one of the prerogatives [special benefits] of the white man, that he may disregard the dictates [rules] of moral principles, when an Indian shall be concerned? . . . "

Source: Murrin, John M. et al. *Liberty, Equality, Power: A History of the American People*. Harcourt Brace. Orlando: 1999, p. 419.

1. Finding the Main Idea What is the main idea of the Jackson passage?

_____

_____

Critical Thinking Skills Activity (continued)

2. **Identifying Points of View** What is President Jackson's view of Native Americans?

   _____

   _____

3. **Finding the Main Idea** What is the main idea of the Frelinghuysen passage?

   _____

   _____

4. **Identifying Points of View** How does Senator Frelinghuysen view Native Americans?

   _____

   _____

✓ Applying the Skill

Directions: Use the excerpts to answer the following questions. Circle the letter of the correct answer.

1. Which of the following would President Jackson be most likely to support?
   A. laws protecting national forests and wilderness areas
   B. laws preserving Native American historical sites and landmarks
   C. laws supporting growth of industry
   D. laws limiting westward expansion of the United States

2. Which word below best describes Senator Frelinghuysen's feelings about the treatment of Native Americans?
   A. helpful
   B. unfaithful
   C. sympathetic
   D. respectful

3. How might President Jackson view of people differ with Senator Frelinghuysen's point of view?
   A. He supports their views.
   B. He does not support their views.
   C. He thinks that they are well educated.
   D. He has no opinion on their views.

Name_____ Date_____ Class_____

Geography and History Activity
The Jackson Era

Chapter

The Elections of 1828 and 1832

Although he won the popular vote, Andrew Jackson lost the presidential election of 1824 to John Quincy Adams. Jackson's highly questioned defeat was the result of no candidate winning the majority of the electoral votes. In such events, the House of Representatives selects the president. They chose Adams.

The Election of 1828

Andrew Jackson ran again in 1828. Prior to 1828, the Republican Party was the only political party. It was one party made up of groups of people with many different views. By 1828, the party had split. The Democratic-Republicans favored state's rights and mistrusted strong central government. Immigrants, laborers in big cities, and people at the frontier were drawn to the Democratic-Republican Party.

The National Republicans again backed Adams. Many National Republicans were merchants or farmers. The National Republicans favored a strong central government and high tariffs to protect Northern manufacturers. They also supported the national bank, called the Bank of the United States. About one-fifth of the money in the Bank of the United States was federal money. The bank was authorized to issue notes, make loans, and hold deposits. The idea of a national bank was controversial and Jackson was suspicious of its power.

Jackson won the election of 1828 with 56 percent of the popular vote and 178 electoral votes to Adams's 83. Being a resident of Tennessee, Jackson was the first president elected from west of the Appalachian Mountains.

The Election of 1832

Jackson ran for reelection in 1832. This was the first election in which candidates were chosen by national nominating conventions. Jackson won 77 percent of the electoral votes, but only about 55 percent of the popular vote. During his second term, Jackson vetoed a bill to renew the 1816 charter of the Bank of the United States. Jackson withdrew all federal money from the Bank of the United States and deposited it in various state banks.

The Presidential Election of 1832

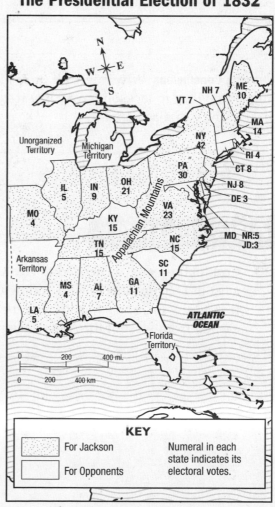

Geography and History Activity (continued)

✓ Applying Geography to History

Directions: Answer the following questions in the spaces provided.

1. **Describing** Describe Jackson's position on the national bank. What actions did he take in regard to it?

   _____

   _____

   _____

2. **Identifying** Which four states in the Northeast formed a cluster of support for Jackson's opponents?

   _____

   _____

   _____

3. **Drawing Conclusions** Why might all presidents previous to Jackson have come from east of the Appalachians?

   _____

   _____

   _____

4. **Assessing** Assume that in the election of 1832, Jackson's opponents won the states of Virginia, North Carolina, Georgia, Alabama, Mississippi, and Louisiana. This would have given the opponents more states than Jackson. Would the results of the election have changed if Jackson's opponents won these states? Explain.

   _____

   _____

5. **Making Connections** Why do you think National Republicans were more likely to favor a National Bank?

   _____

   _____

   _____

GOING FURTHER ▶ ▶▶▶

- Conduct research as needed to create a list of U.S. presidents who, following in Andrew Jackson's footsteps, were elected from west of the Appalachian Mountains. Create a simple map indicating the home state of each of these presidents.

Chapter

Linking Past and Present Activity

The Jackson Era

Political Campaigns

THEN Many political campaigning techniques originated in the 1840 presidential campaign, in which the Democratic incumbent, Martin Van Buren, opposed the Whig candidate, William Henry Harrison. Harrison repeatedly attacked Van Buren for being an aristocrat who was not interested in the depression and the high unemployment rate. Harrison then shifted focus away from his own wealthy background by running on the strength of his military career.

The Whigs selected John Tyler as Harrison's running mate. They coined a catchy slogan to capture the public's imagination: "Tippecanoe and Tyler, Too." The slogan referred to Harrison's military victory at the Battle of Tippecanoe. Their strategy paid off—Harrison won 234 presidential electoral votes compared to 60 for Van Buren.

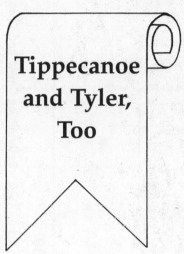

Tippecanoe and Tyler, Too

NOW More than 160 years later, candidates still use many of the same campaign techniques. Political candidates have slogans, rallies, and campaign buttons. Today the electronic media also play a major part in political campaigns. Candidates spend campaign funds on radio and television advertising to reach many voters. Candidates receive contributions from political action committees and their supporters, and they can earn matching funds from the government.

Political campaigns are much more expensive today than in 1840. For example, candidates for the United States House and Senate in 2004 spent a total of more than $1 billion seeking office.

Directions: Match each candidate in Column A with his slogan in Column B. Write the correct letters in the blanks. You may need to research to find the correct answers.

Column A

_____ **1.** Andrew Jackson

_____ **2.** Harry S. Truman

_____ **3.** James Monroe

_____ **4.** Dwight D. Eisenhower

_____ **5.** Abraham Lincoln

_____ **6.** Martin Van Buren

Column B

A. I Like Ike

B. Van's popularity fills the great West; His firmness and honesty none can contest

C. Let the People Rule

D. I'm Just Wild About Harry

E. Era of Good Feelings

F. Honest Old Abe

Time Line Activity

The Jackson Era

Growth of Democracy (1815–1840)

Direction: Use your textbook and the information in the time line to answer the questions in the spaces provided.

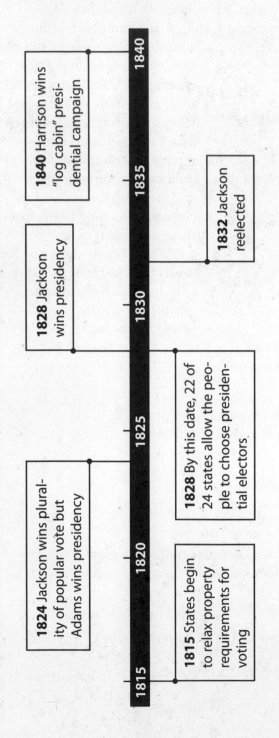

1840 Harrison wins "log cabin" presidential campaign

1828 Jackson wins presidency

1832 Jackson reelected

1824 Jackson wins plurality of popular vote but Adams wins presidency

1828 By this date, 22 of 24 states allow the people to choose presidential electors.

1815 States begin to relax property requirements for voting

1815 | 1820 | 1825 | 1830 | 1835 | 1840

Background

After 1800, the new Western states began to have greater influence in elections. In addition, most states began to eliminate the property ownership requirement for voters. By 1828, most states no longer allowed state legislatures to choose presidential electors. Instead, the citizens of the state made the selection. As a result, Andrew Jackson was able to win election twice, and "log cabin" candidates became popular.

Analyzing the Time Line

1. **Identifying** In what year did Jackson first run for president, and what was the result?

_____

_____

2. **Calculating** How many presidential elections did Andrew Jackson win?

_____

_____

3. **Determining Cause and Effect** What change in state laws allowed more people to vote?

_____

_____

4. **Explaining** How did 22 states change the rules for presidential elections by 1828?

_____

_____

School-to-Home Connection Activity
The Jackson Era

What Do You Know?

Directions: Ask each other the following questions to see how much you know about the Jackson era.*

Student: What are favorite sons?

Partner's answer:

Student's answer:

Partner: Where did the "Five Civilized Tribes" originally live?

Student: Who was Osceola?

Partner's answer:

Student's answer:

Partner: What is the laissez-faire principle?

*With your student, find answers to these questions in the student textbook.

Name_____ Date_____ Class_____

 School-to-Home Connection Activity (continued)

Understanding the Essential Questions

Directions: Rewrite each Essential Question as a statement. Then use your textbook to help you write details that support your statement in the graphic organizer provided.

Section 1 How did political beliefs and events shape Andrew Jackson's presidency?

Statement: _____

Political Beliefs and Events		Effect on Jackson's Presidency
Jackson declared "equal protection and equal benefits" for all white American men.	⇨	
Democrats wanted to open up government jobs to people from all walks of life.	⇨	
Jackson's supporters stopped using the caucus, system in which members of Congress chose major candidates.	⇨	

Section 2 How did Andrew Jackson's presidency affect Native Americans?

Statement: _____

Attitude or Event		How It Affected Native Americans
Jackson's frontier background led him to support the settlers' demand for Native American land and push the Indian Removal Act through Congress.	⇨	
Jackson supported Georgia's efforts to remove the Cherokee, and the federal government persuaded some Cherokee to sign The Treaty of New Echota.	⇨	

Section 3 How do economic issues affect the president and presidential elections?

Statement: _____

Effects on the President	Effects on Presidential Elections

Reteaching Activity

The Jackson Era

Andrew Jackson brought a spirit of equality to American politics. On most issues, President Jackson acted on behalf of ordinary Americans. The rights of certain groups, however, were not always protected, especially those of Native Americans. In spite of this, Jackson's views had a far-reaching effect on government policies.

Creating a Fishbone Diagram   **DIRECTIONS:** Each phrase listed below relates to a topic on the diagram. Write the phrase next to the topic it supports. Then summarize Jackson's view about the topic.

Dade Massacre	**nominating conventions**	**suffrage expanded**
Force Bill	**Nullification Act**	**Trail of Tears**
government deposits withdrawn	**secession threat**	**veto of charter bill**
Indian Removal Act	**spoils system**	***Worcester v. Georgia***

Democracy

Summary of Jackson's View:

Tariff Debate

Summary of Jackson's View:

President Andrew Jackson

Native Americans

Summary of Jackson's View:

Bank of the United States

Summary of Jackson's View:

Section Resources

Guided Reading Activity

The Jackson Era

Jacksonian Democracy

Reading Tip   If you come across a word you do not understand, use context clues to help you figure it out. "Context" refers to the words surrounding an unfamiliar word that provide clues to its meaning.

Reading for Accuracy   DIRECTIONS: Use your textbook to decide if a statement is true or false. Write **T** or **F** in the blank. If a statement is false, rewrite it to make it true.

_____ **1.** Andrew Jackson received a majority of the electoral votes in the election of 1824.

_____

_____ **2.** By 1828, the Republican Party had split into the Democratic-Republicans and the National Republicans.

_____

_____ **3.** The National Republicans favored states' rights and mistrusted a strong central government.

_____

_____ **4.** During Jackson's administration, more white men were able to take part in the political process than previously.

_____

_____ **5.** The practice of replacing government employees with an election winner's supporters is known as the caucus system.

_____

_____ **6.** Nominating conventions replaced caucuses for choosing presidential candidates.

_____

_____ **7.** Tariffs were the main issue that prompted South Carolina to pass the Nullification Act.

_____

Copyright © Glencoe/McGraw-Hill, a division of The McGraw-Hill Companies, Inc.

Guided Reading Activity

The Jackson Era

Conflicts Over Land

Reading Tip   It is important to focus on your reading assignment. Make time to read a section, and pay attention to it as you read.

Outlining   DIRECTIONS: As you read the section, complete the outline below.

I. Moving Native Americans

  A. The _____ Tribes lived in the Southeast in farming societies.

  B. The _____ Act allowed the federal government to pay Native Americans to move west of the Mississippi River.

  C. The _____, in present-day Oklahoma, was an area that was set aside for Native American relocation.

  D. Supreme Court Chief Justice _____ ruled that the state of Georgia could not interfere with the Cherokee.

  E. The forced journey west by the Cherokee people is called the

  _____.

II. Native American Resistance

  A. The Sauk and Fox people attempted to recapture their homeland in

  _____.

  B. The _____ people were the only Native Americans to successfully resist removal.

  C. Chief _____ led his people in fighting against white settlers and soldiers in Florida.

  D. Native Americans who resettled west of the Mississippi River lived on

  _____ and were organized by _____.

Copyright © Glencoe/McGraw-Hill, a division of The McGraw-Hill Companies, Inc.

Name_____ Date_____ Class_____

Guided Reading Activity

The Jackson Era

Section

Jackson and the Bank

Reading Tip

Does this section seem long to you? Divide this reading assignment into smaller tasks. Try reading and understanding just half of the section now. Then come back later and finish the section.

Filling in the Blanks   DIRECTIONS: Use your textbook to fill in the blanks using the words in the box. Some words may not be used.

Henry Clay	veto	Whigs
Republicans	depression	treasury
Martin Van Buren	Bank of the United States	William Henry Harrison
John Tyler	laissez-faire	sectional
approval	national	James Polk

The **(1)** _____ became a central issue in the 1832 presidential election. Senators

Daniel Webster and **(2)** _____ hoped President Jackson's **(3)** _____ of

the institution's new charter would lead to his defeat. However, their strategy failed, and

Jackson was reelected. In the 1836 election, Vice President **(4)** _____ faced

opposition from a new political party, the **(5)** _____.

The Panic of 1837 was the beginning of an economic **(6)** _____. To address bank

failures, business closures, and the decline of investments, an independent federal

(7) _____ was established. This was an example of the **(8)** _____

principle that Government should stay out of the nation's economy as much as possible.

The Whig party gained power in 1840 with the presidential election

of **(9)** _____, who died in office. His successor, former Vice President

(10) _____, made decisions that were considered disloyal to the Whigs. Members

of that party were voting more and more along **(11)** _____ lines. As a result, the

Whigs lost the 1844 election to the Democratic candidate, **(12)** _____.

41

Chapter Resources

Manifest Destiny

Name_____ Date_____ Class_____

Content Vocabulary Activity

Manifest Destiny

Identifying **DIRECTIONS:** Select a term from the list below to complete the sentences that follow.

joint occupation	rancho	prairie schooners
empresario	forty-niners	Tejanos
Californios	Manifest Destiny	ceded
vigilante	mountain men	boomtown
rendezvous	decree	emigrants
annex	ranchero	

In the early 1800s, Secretary of State John Quincy Adams worked out an agreement with

Britain. In this agreement, the United States and Great Britain could have

(1) _____ of the Oregon Country. The first non-Native Americans to come to this

area were fur traders, known as **(2)** _____. Every year, these traders met for a

(3) _____ with the trading companies. Soon, settlers called **(4)** _____

began migrating to Oregon in their canvas-covered wagons called **(5)** _____.

As more people settled throughout the United States, they thought it was their right to extend

the country's boundaries all the way to the Pacific Ocean. They believed in **(6)** _____.

Around the same time, the United States purchased the Louisiana Territory from France.

Americans felt that the land in present-day Texas was part of that purchase. Most residents of

Texas, however, were **(7)** _____, or Mexicans who claimed the land as their home.

Because the Spanish wanted to promote growth, they used a(n) **(8)** _____ to recruit

settlers to move to Texas. By 1830, Americans in Texas outnumbered Mexicans. The Mexican

government was alarmed at the American influence and issued a(n) **(9)** _____ to

stop all immigration from the United States into Texas. After the battle for Texas independence,

the settlers elected Sam Houston as their president. Houston requested that the United States

(10) _____, or take control of, Texas. Andrew Jackson refused Houston's request,

and Texas remained an independent country.

Content Vocabulary Activity (continued)

In 1821 after Mexico gained its independence from Spain, California became a state.

A Mexican settler, called a(n) **(11)** _____, would buy an available tract of land and

set up a large ranch called a(n) **(12)** _____. Native Americans, who worked the

land in return for food and shelter, were treated almost like enslaved people by the ranch

owner, known as a(n) **(13)** _____.

The U.S. government wanted to protect its borders and own all connecting land. It offered

to purchase California and New Mexico from Mexico. The leaders of Mexico refused. The

United States felt that it had no choice but to invade. The battle was long and hard fought. By

mid-September 1847, the American forces had won. In what was called the Mexican Cession,

Mexico finally **(14)** _____ California and New Mexico to the United States.

When gold was discovered in California in 1848, people from all over the world traveled to the

region in search of riches. People who arrived in 1849 were known as **(15)** _____.

As more and more people arrived, they built and lived in a community called a(n)

(16) _____. These communities were built almost overnight. To protect

themselves, citizens formed a(n) **(17)** _____ group because there were no police.

Academic Vocabulary Activity
Manifest Destiny

Academic Words in This Chapter

access	establish	commence	incorporate
resource	remove	constitution	

A. Word Meaning Activity: Identifying Synonyms

Directions: Read the underlined words below, as well as the four words or phrases next to them. Circle the word or phrase that is *most similar* in meaning to the underlined word as it is used in the chapter.

1. <u>access</u>:   exclude, ability to get to, refuse to permit, prohibit

2. <u>resource</u>:   routine, creative, source of wealth, authority

3. <u>establish</u>:   set up, phase out, abolish, terminate

4. <u>remove</u>:   adhere, place, take away, insert

5. <u>commence</u>:   finish, begin, graduate, pay for

6. <u>constitution</u>: fundamental laws, consisting of, organization, result

7. <u>incorporate</u>: exclusive, justify, purchase, include

Copyright © Glencoe/McGraw-Hill, a division of The McGraw-Hill Companies, Inc.

Academic Vocabulary Activity (continued)

B. Word Family Activity: Completing a Word Chart

Directions: A *noun* is a word that names a person, a place, a thing, or an idea. Examples include *president, Chicago, army,* and *slavery*. A *verb* is a word that is used to describe an action, an experience, or a state of being. Examples include *govern, attempt,* and *seem*. An *adjective* is a word that is used to describe a noun. Examples include *interesting, numeric,* and *comical*. Some words have more than one form. Place a check mark (√) in the appropriate column.

Words	Noun	Verb	Adjective
1. accessed			
2. accessible			
3. access			
4. resource			
5. resourceful			
6. establish			
7. establishment			
8. established			
9. removed			
10. removal			
11. commence			
12. constitution			
13. incorporate			

Primary Source Readings

Manifest Destiny

Courage Beyond His Years

Interpreting the Source

Beginning in 1841, wagon trains of emigrants traveled more than 2,000 miles (3,128.68 km) to California. On their journey, emigrants faced injury, disease, broken equipment, attacks by Native Americans, and crossing the Rocky Mountains. Seventeen-year-old Moses Schallenberger was part of a group that left for California in May of 1844. He kept a diary about his experiences. Because of heavy snowfall, Moses and two other men stayed to guard wagons and cargo as the rest of the party crossed the mountains. Later, the two older guards also decided to cross the mountains on foot, but the trip was too hard for Moses, and he volunteered to remain alone.

Amazingly, everyone in the group survived the winter and arrived safely in California.

Guided Reading

As you read, note how Moses's mood changes during these winter months.

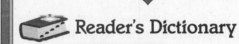

Reader's Dictionary

sapling: a young tree
rawhide: an animal skin with fur removed
pine knots: pinewood used for fuel

The morning after the separation of our party, we set about making a cabin. . . . We cut **saplings**. . . . These we formed into a rude house, and we covered it with **rawhides** and pine brush. On the evening of the day we finished our little house it began to snow. . . . It kept on snowing continually . . . and we began to fear that we would perish in the snow. . . . We determined to start for California on foot.

We did not say much at the parting. The feeling of loneliness that came over me as the . . . men turned away I cannot express, though it will never be forgotten. . . . As soon [as] I was able to crawl around next morning, I put on my snow-shoes, and, taking my rifle, scoured the country thoroughly for foxes. The result was . . . plenty of tracks, no fox.

Discouraged and sick at heart, I came in . . . and my eyes fell upon some steel traps that Captain Stevens had left behind in his wagon. . . . My spirits began to rise immediately. . . . That night I went to bed with a lighter heart, and was able to get some sleep.

As soon as daylight came I went out to inspect the traps. . . . To my great delight I found in one of them a starved coyote. . . . I ate his meat, but it was horrible. . . . For three days that was all I had to eat. On the third night I caught two foxes. I roasted one of them, and the meat . . . was delicious.

I never really suffered for something to eat, but was in almost continual anxiety for fear the supply would give out. My only hope was that the supply of foxes would not become exhausted. . . . I had just coffee enough for one cup, and that I saved for Christmas.

Primary Source Readings (continued)

> The daily struggle and the uncertainty under which I labored were very wearing. I was always worried and anxious, not about myself alone, but in regard to those who had gone forward. . . . Fortunately, I had plenty of books, Dr. Townsend having brought out quite a library. . . . I used often to read aloud, for I longed for some sound to break the oppressive stillness. At night I built large fires and read by the light of the **pine knots** as late as possible. . . . I thought the snow would never leave the ground, and the few months I had been living here seemed like years.
>
> One evening, a little before sunset . . . I could distinguish the figure of a man moving toward me. . . . I recognized the familiar face of Dennis Martin. My feelings can be better imagined than described.

Source: *Pioneer Children on the Journey West.* Boulder, Colorado: Westview Press, 1995.

DBQ Document-Based Questions

Directions: Answer the questions below in the spaces provided.

1. **Specifying** What is the first thing the guards did after the rest of their group left?

_____

_____

2. **Identifying** Who are the people Moses is worried and anxious about?

_____

_____

3. **Describing** What lifts Moses's spirits?

_____

_____

4. **Explaining** Why does Moses read aloud?

_____

_____

5. **Speculating** What do you think is the most difficult thing Moses had to face?

_____

_____

Name_____ Date_____ Class_____

Writing Skills Activity

Manifest Destiny

Identifying Sequence of Activities

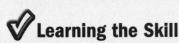 **Learning the Skill**

In your classes, you may be asked to explain a process (such as how a bill is passed) or tell someone how to do something (such as how to hook up a DVD player to the TV). To do this, you will need to list, in order, the sequence of activities needed to achieve the desired result. This type of writing is often referred to as technical writing.

Follow these steps when writing a technical document:

- Consider the process or activity you are defining.
- List, in order, the steps needed. Numbering your steps will reinforce that the activities must follow that order.
- Review what you have written. Verify that the steps are presented correctly and that no information has been left out.
- Make any revisions necessary to finalize your document.

 Practicing the Skill

Directions: The information listed below contains the steps needed to make flour tortillas. Number the actions in the sequence in which they are performed.

_____ Divide your dough into 8 balls of equal size, cover them, and let them rest for 20 minutes.

_____ Gather the following ingredients: 2 cups flour, 1½ teaspoons baking powder, 1 teaspoon salt, 2 tablespoons vegetable oil, ¾ cup lukewarm milk.

_____ Stir together the first two ingredients. Whisk together the remaining ingredients. Gradually add the milk mixture to the flour, and work the mixture into a dough.

_____ Dust your work surface with flour. Take a ball of dough, and roll it out until you have a 7- or 8-inch tortilla.

_____ Place the finished tortilla in a napkin-lined basket and cover.

_____ Transfer the tortilla to a hot, dry skillet. Cook for 30 seconds, turn, and cook the other side for 30 seconds.

_____ Turn the dough out onto a surface dusted with flour. Knead vigorously for about 2 minutes. Return the dough to the bowl, cover with a damp cloth, and let it rest for 15 minutes.

Writing Skills Activity (continued)

✓ Applying the Skill

Directions: Imagine you are living near St. Louis, Missouri, in the 1850s. Your family has decided to move to Oregon. The list below includes some of the activities your family should accomplish. Add to the list four other activities, then put all the activities in the order in which they should be accomplished.

_____ Make camp for night at Shawnee Mission, Kansas.

_____ Load wagon onto steamship at St. Louis for upstream journey.

_____ Sell excess goods at Fort Laramie, Wyoming.

_____ Purchase prairie schooner.

_____ Organize traveling party for overland journey after disembarking in Independence.

_____ Pack wagon with supplies.

_____

_____

_____

_____

_____

_____

_____

_____

Self-Assessment Checklist

Assess your list using the checklist below:

☐ I added four more activities.

☐ I reviewed and understood all activities.

☐ I listed the steps in a logical order.

☐ I reviewed and verified that the steps are presented correctly.

Social Studies Skills Activity

Manifest Destiny

Reading a Time Line

 Learning the Skill

Historians create time lines to show a chronology of key events during a particular historical period. A time line begins with a specific date and ends with another one. All the events between these dates happened in the order in which they are listed—either from left to right or top to bottom. Reading time lines is an easy way to make sense of the flow of events and when they occurred. A time line also gives you a picture of history and the relationships among events.

Use the following steps to read a time line:

- Read the title of the time line to understand what topic is being chronicled.
- Determine the time span, or the beginning and ending dates.
- Determine the time intervals. This is the length of the smaller segments of time used to divide the period on the time line.
- Identify the individual events labeled along the time line. Look for relationships among the events.

 Practicing the Skill

Directions: Read the information on the time line below, and then answer the questions that follow.

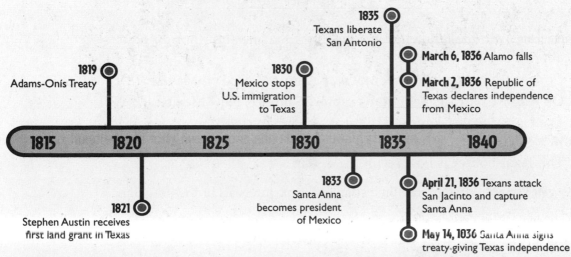

Texas War for Independence

1. **Calculating** What is the time span for this time line? What are the intervals on this time line?

_____

Social Studies Skills Activity (continued)

2. **Identifying** When did Austin receive his land grant in Texas?

_____

3. **Calculating** How much time passed between when Santa Anna was captured and when he signed the treaty?

_____

4. **Analyzing** Did Texas declare independence from Mexico before or after Texans liberated San Antonio?

_____

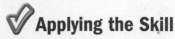 **Applying the Skill**

Directions: Read the information on the time line below, and then follow the instructions and answer the questions that follow on a separate piece of paper.

Mexican–American War

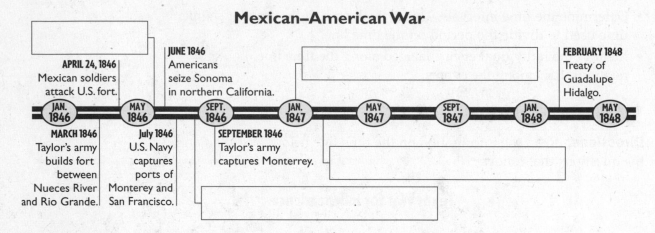

APRIL 24, 1846
Mexican soldiers attack U.S. fort.

JUNE 1846
Americans seize Sonoma in northern California.

FEBRUARY 1848
Treaty of Guadalupe Hidalgo.

JAN. 1846 — MAY 1846 — SEPT. 1846 — JAN. 1847 — MAY 1847 — SEPT. 1847 — JAN. 1848 — MAY 1848

MARCH 1846
Taylor's army builds fort between Nueces River and Rio Grande.

July 1846
U.S. Navy captures ports of Monterey and San Francisco.

SEPTEMBER 1846
Taylor's army captures Monterrey.

1. **Sequencing** Add the following events to the time line at the appropriate location:
   - Congress passes a declaration of war against Mexico on May 11, 1846.
   - On August 18, 1846, Americans capture Santa Fe, New Mexico.
   - The United States controls California in January 1847.
   - In February 1847, Taylor's army defeats the Mexicans at Buena Vista. The Texas border is now secure.

2. **Analyzing Visuals** What are the time span and time intervals of the time line?

3. **Identifying** What three present-day states were territories involved in the Mexican-American War? Which was secured first?

Differentiated Instruction Activity

Manifest Destiny

Gold at Sutter's Mill

Read the following excerpt from James Marshall regarding his discovery of gold at Sutter's Mill, in January 1848 near present-day Coloma, California. Then answer the questions that follow.

[A]bout half past seven o'clock on or about the 19th of January—I am not quite certain to a day, but it was between the 18th and 20th of that month—1848, I went down [to the tail race in the mill] as usual, and after shutting off the water from the race, I stepped into it, near the lower end, and there, upon the rock, about six inches beneath the surface of the water, I discovered the gold. I was entirely alone at the time. I picked up one or two pieces and examined them attentively; and having some general knowledge of minerals, I could not call to mind more than two which in any way resembled this—sulphuret of iron, very bright and brittle; and gold, bright, yet malleable; I then tried it between two rocks, and found that it could be beaten into a different shape, but not broken. I then collected four or five pieces and went up to Mr. Scott . . . and said, "I have found it." . . .

[Others were called to see the gold.] About 10 o'clock the same morning, P.L. Wimmer came down from the house, and was very much surprised at the discovery . . . which he took home to show his wife, who, the next day, made some experiments upon it by boiling it in strong lye, and saleratus; and Mr. Bennet by my directions beat it very thin.

Four days afterwards, I went to the Fort for provisions, and carried with me about three ounces of the gold, which Capt. Sutter and I tested with nitric acid. I then tried it in Sutter's presence by taking three silver dollars and balancing them by the dust in the air, then immersed both in water, and the superior weight of the gold satisfied us both of its nature and value.

Source: James W. Marshall. "Gold Strike at Sutter's Mill." Excerpted in *Eyewitness to America*. Edited by David Colbert. New York: Vintage Books, 1998.

Directions: Use the information from the excerpt and your textbook to answer the following questions on a separate sheet of paper.

1. **Listing** Identify the steps James Marshall took to verify that his discovery was gold.

2. **Making Inferences** Prices soared in the boom economy. For example, eggs might sell for 50 cents each, and potatoes went for up to $1 a pound. Why do you think this occurred?

Differentiated Instruction Activity (continued)

The following activities are ways the basic lesson can be modified to accommodate students' different learning styles.

English Language Learner (ELL)

Have students identify words and phrases from the passage that can help them organize the information sequentially. Then have them create a time line of the events in the excerpt.

Gifted and Talented

The discovery of gold at Sutter's Mill helped transform California from a Mexican frontier province to an American territory as thousands of settlers poured into the region in search of prosperity and a better life. California continues to be a magnet for immigrants from all over the world. Ask students to investigate the evolution of economic and political power in California from just before the Gold Rush to the present day and present their findings in a four-page paper.

Verbal/Linguistic; Intrapersonal

Have students write several diary entries from the perspective of a miner who has *not* succeeded in finding much gold.

Visual/Spatial

Ask students to find three examples of art pertaining to the Gold Rush in the library media center or online. Direct students to artists such as A.D.O. Browere, William Smith Jewett, and Charles Christian Nahl. For each piece, students should identify the artist and title and write one paragraph about what they see happening. Have students pay special attention to the people, objects, and activities depicted.

Kinesthetic

Have students research various aspects of the boomtowns that often grew around mining sites. Then ask them to create a model of a typical boomtown, complete with feed store, general store, blacksmith shop, and so on. Invite students to present and explain their models to the class.

Naturalist

Ask students to investigate the various ways gold was mined during the Gold Rush. Then have them assess the impact of mining on California's environment and present their findings in a three-page paper.

Interpersonal

Have students work with a partner to write a dialogue that might have occurred in one of the following situations: a husband and wife in Indiana discuss the possibility of going west in search of gold; James Marshall and Captain Sutter talk about Marshall's discovery; two miners have a dispute over a mining claim. Students may consult whatever reference materials they wish to help them with this assignment.

Name_____ Date_____ Class_____

Critical Thinking Skills Activity
Manifest Destiny

Predicting Consequences

✔ Learning the Skill

When you read history, you can sometimes predict consequences based on certain events or conditions. For example, you might read that gold was discovered on a certain date in a remote area of California. As a result, you might predict that the population of that area would increase because prospectors would travel to the area to look for gold. Being able to predict consequences can help you better understand the sequence of historical events.

✔ Practicing the Skill

Directions: Read the following passage, and then answer the questions that follow.

> The area of North America west of the Rocky Mountains remained remote in the early 1800s. Up until the 1830s, there were few people other than mountain men and fur traders in the Oregon country. Oregon was also disputed territory in the early 1800s, with claims by the United States, Britain, Spain, and Russia.
>
> In 1818 the United States and Britain arranged for joint occupation of Oregon. In 1819 Spain gave up its claim to Oregon. Russia, concentrating on Alaska, gave up its claim to Oregon in 1824. Lured by stories of abundant, fertile land, the emigration of United States citizens to Oregon increased during the 1830s and 1840s. By the mid-1840s, the population of United States citizens in Oregon had increased to 5,000, whereas the British population was only about 700. Most United States citizens came over the 2,000-mile-long Oregon Trail, from Independence, Missouri, to the mouth of the Columbia River. Portland was the gateway to the wet, fertile Willamette River valley where most people settled. By 1846 Britain and the United States resolved the dispute over Oregon.

1. **Analyzing** What would you expect to be the consequence of both the United States and Britain occupying the Oregon Territory?

_____

_____

2. **Predicting** Consider the population in Oregon in the mid-1840s. Which country would you predict would eventually own Oregon?

_____

_____

Critical Thinking Skills Activity (continued)

3. **Making Connections** How did the location of Oregon contribute to the struggle to control the area?

_____

_____

_____

4. **Predicting** Gold was discovered in California in 1848. Predict the consequences of this discovery on the population and settlement of Oregon.

_____

_____

_____

✓ Applying the Skill

Directions: After reading the passage about Oregon, answer the following questions. Circle the letter of the correct answer.

1. Which of the following was a consequence of the many early European explorations of Oregon?
   A. Maps of Oregon were not very accurate.
   B. Many countries claimed land in the Oregon region.
   C. No one ever returned to Oregon.
   D. Americans were the only people who were interested in Oregon.

2. What might have happened if Britain had not been willing to settle its dispute with the United States over Oregon in 1846?
   A. The United States would have given up its claim.
   B. The Oregon Trail would have been closed.
   C. The United States and Britain could have gone to war.
   D. Britain would have gone to war with France.

3. How do you think the arrival of new American settlers in Oregon would affect the local Native American populations?
   A. The new settlements would have no effect on them.
   B. The population of Native Americans would increase.
   C. Native Americans from other areas would move to Oregon.
   D. The population of Native Americans would decrease.

Geography and History Activity
Manifest Destiny

Ranches of the Southwest: A Manifest Destiny

The southwestern United States was under Spanish and Hispanic rule from the time of Coronado's explorations in 1540 until the end of the Mexican-American War in 1848. During Spain's rule, the area was divided into three provinces: New Mexico, California, and Tejas (Texas). The vast province of New Mexico included what is now the state of New Mexico, most of Colorado and Arizona, and parts of Utah, Wyoming, Kansas, Oklahoma, and Texas. In 1821 Mexico won independence from Spain and took over the rule of these areas.

The First Ranches

When the Spanish settled in the Southwest, they introduced animals, plants, and farming methods that continue to influence the economy and lifestyle of this region today. The Spanish were the first to bring horses, cattle, and sheep to the Southwest. These animals thrived in the dry climate where the vegetation was similar to what was found in Spain.

The Southwest is well-known for its ranches, both large and small. Ranching, cowhands, cattle drives, and the open range, where livestock can roam and feed without fences, all began in the Spanish Southwest. The original Spanish missions maintained large animal herds. The missionaries trained Native Americans in the skills of the vaqueros, or herders on horses. The vaqueros were the forerunners of cowhands, and the equipment and techniques they used were well suited to the open-range style of ranching. The clothing worn by cowhands, the gear for their horses, and the techniques for roping and herding cattle originated with the Spanish.

Cattle Country in Texas

The Spanish missions of Texas, such as the one in San Antonio, maintained huge herds of cattle. Cattle that strayed from the missions or that wandered north from Mexico ran wild on the vast open plains of Texas. These strays were the legendary Texas longhorns; their horns could span six feet. They had good survival instincts, were sturdy, and could adapt to any environment. The longhorn population multiplied quickly, reaching its peak in 1865.

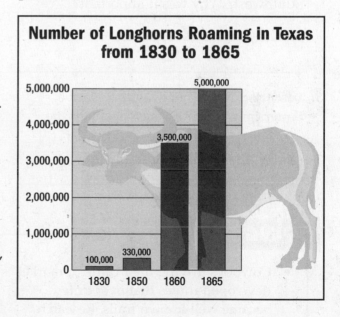

Number of Longhorns Roaming in Texas from 1830 to 1865

Year	Number
1830	100,000
1850	330,000
1860	3,500,000
1865	5,000,000

Geography and History Activity (continued)

Longhorns provided stock for the huge open-range ranches that later developed in Texas. The vaquero evolved into the Texan cowhand. Texans started long cattle drives to take their longhorns to market. Cattle drives and cowhands have since become a popular part of American culture. Spanish missions and settlers not only provided the Southwest with the perfect animals and plants, but they also introduced a way of life that came to symbolize "America."

✓ Applying Geography to History

Directions: Use the information in this activity to answer the following questions in the spaces provided.

1. **Listing** What current states, or parts of states, were included in the Southwest provinces controlled by Spain?

_____

_____

2. **Comparing** In what important way was Spain's climate similar to that of the Southwest? Why was it important?

_____

_____

3. **Describing** Name one way that Native Americans benefited from Spanish rule.

_____

_____

4. **Determining Cause and Effect** Why did the longhorn population in Texas multiply so quickly?

_____

_____

5. **Analyzing** Explain how the Spanish influenced the lifestyle and economy of the Southwest.

_____

_____

_____

GOING FURTHER ▶ ▶▶▶

- Cowboys driving their cattle to market developed routes that over time became well-known trails. Research Texas cattle trails, such as the Shawnee Trail, the Goodnight-Loving Trail, or the Chisolm Trail. Find information about what a typical day might be like on the trail. How long might a cowhand spend in the saddle? What did a cowhand eat? How long did a drive take, and how many cattle could be driven at one time? Write a report describing your findings.

Chapter

Linking Past and Present Activity
Manifest Destiny

Traveling Cross-Country

THEN In the early 1800s, pioneers generally traveled by Conestoga wagons. These covered wagons were known as the "camels of the prairie" because they could make long, hard journeys without breaking down.

The Pennsylvania Dutch designed the Conestoga wagon to carry freight. To prevent items from falling out of the wagon, both ends of the wagon were higher than the middle, and the bottom was slightly curved. The back wheels of the Conestoga were larger than the front wheels. All of the wheels had wide iron bands that enabled the wagon to travel on dirt roads without getting bogged down in the mud. Originally teams of four to six horses pulled the wagons, but the pioneers often used oxen or mules. The wagons could transport entire families and all their possessions as well as all supplies necessary for a 2,000-mile (3,218 km), six-month journey.

NOW Transportation changed enormously in the United States since the early 1800s. Today people can travel across the United States in less than a day in airplanes, or they can drive automobiles or ride on trains.

After the railroad building boom of the 1840s, Conestoga wagons no longer hauled the country's freight. Railroads' speed and freight capacity were huge improvements over covered wagons. Today railroads still carry freight.

A network of paved highways has replaced the dirt roads of the early 1800s. In 1956 the construction of the interstate highway system began. Today, highways crisscross the nation and connect major cities throughout the United States. Once only brave pioneers crossed the country, but now many Americans make this journey.

Making a List   DIRECTIONS:
Think about the size of a Conestoga wagon. Now imagine that you are a pioneer taking a six-month, cross-country journey in such a wagon. List 10 things that you would take to keep you supplied and that could fit into the wagon. Remember that there were no grocery or hardware stores along the way!

Item to Bring	Why It Is Essential
1.	
2.	
3.	
4.	
5.	
6.	
7.	
8.	
9.	
10.	

Time Line Activity

Manifest Destiny

The United States Acquires Texas and California (1821–1850)

Directions: Use the following information about Texas and California to complete the time line.

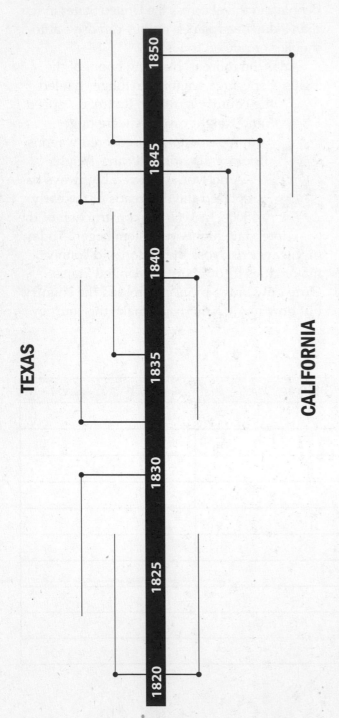

CALIFORNIA

- In 1839 John Sutter built a trading post for Americans who reached California.
- Texas became the 28th state in 1845.
- In 1845 President Polk offered to purchase California from Mexico.
- War with Mexico began in 1846.
- Americans proclaimed California the Bear Flag Republic in 1846.
- California became the 31st state in 1850.

TEXAS

Background

- When Mexico gained independence from Spain in 1821, California became a state of Mexico.
- In 1821 Mexico invited Stephen Austin and Americans to Texas.
- In 1830 Mexico issued a decree to stop U.S. immigration.
- Santa Anna became dictator of Mexico in 1833.
- In 1836 Texas declared independence.
- In the same year, Houston defeated Santa Anna at San Jacinto.

A dispute about the border of Texas ignited the Mexican War. At the end of that war, California completed the expansion of the contiguous United States from the Atlantic to the Pacific.

School-to-Home Connection Activity

Manifest Destiny

What Do You Know?

Directions: Ask each other the following questions to see how much you know about how the idea of Manifest Destiny affected the United States.*

Student: What did the Democrats' slogan "Fifty-four Forty or Fight" mean?

Partner's answer:

Student's answer:

Partner: What did the new settlers agree to do in exchange for cheap land in Texas?

Student: Who was William Becknell?

Partner's answer:

Student's answer:

Partner: Why did California have to wait to become a state?

*With your student, find answers to these questions in the student textbook.

Name_____ Date_____ Class_____

 School-to-Home Connection Activity (continued)

Understanding the Essential Questions

Directions: Rewrite each Essential Question as a statement. Then use your textbook to help you write details that support your statement in the graphic organizer provided.

Section 1 How did the idea of Manifest Destiny influence western settlement?

Statement: _____

The United States was destined to extend its boundaries to the Pacific.	Therefore >	

Section 2 Why did Texans fight for their independence from Mexico?

Statement: _____

Mexican government:	
Texan settlers:	⟹ The fight begins for the independence of Texas.

Section 3 How did Mexican lands in the West become part of the United States?

Statement: _____

Event		How the Land Became Part of the United States
Treaty of Guadalupe Hidalgo	⟹	
Mexican Cession	⟹	
Gadsden Purchase	⟹	

Section 4 What factors affected the settlement of California and Utah in the West?

Statement: _____

California	Utah

Name_____ Date_____ Class_____

Reteaching Activity
Manifest Destiny

In the 1800s, many Americans believed their nation had a "Manifest Destiny" to expand all the way to the Pacific Ocean. By the middle of the century, this mission was fulfilled. The United States added the territories of Oregon, Texas, New Mexico, California, and Utah, expanding the mainland to its present size.

Sequencing   DIRECTIONS: Each item below represents a key event in our nation's expansion. First identify the territory associated with each event. Write O for Oregon, T for Texas, CN for California and New Mexico, or U for Utah next to each event. Then write the number of each item in the proper sequence in the diagram. Note that an event can be used twice.

_____ **1.** battle at Gonzales	_____ **10.** Polk sends troops into disputed area; war begins
_____ **2.** Mexico refuses Polk's offer to buy	_____ **11.** Spain gives up claim in Adams-Onís Treaty
_____ **3.** Scott captures Mexico City	_____ **12.** Brigham Young leads migration to Salt Lake
_____ **4.** Congress votes to annex	_____ **13.** Britain agrees to border at 49° N latitude
_____ **5.** Bear Flag Republic declared	_____ **14.** Mexican decree bans American settlers
_____ **6.** setters establish Deseret	_____ **15.** Polk elected on slogan "Fifty-Four Forty or Fight"
_____ **7.** Britain agrees to joint occupation	_____ **16.** Treaty of Guadalupe Hidalgo
_____ **8.** Smith founds Mormon Church	_____ **17.** Santa Anna captured at San Jacinto
_____ **9.** the Alamo falls	

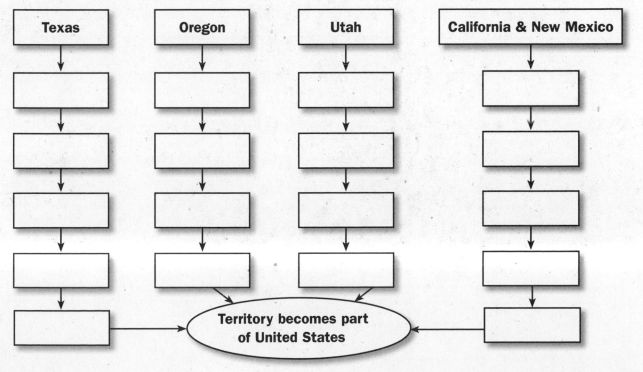

Section Resources

Name_____ Date_____ Class_____

Guided Reading Activity

Manifest Destiny

Section

The Oregon Country

Reading Tip   For a quick reference guide, create an outline for the section using the headings as the main ideas. Include supporting details and key words.

Answering Questions   **DIRECTIONS:** As you read the section, answer the questions below.

1. **Listing** List the four nations that claimed the Oregon Country.

_____

2. **Explaining** What did Spain agree to do in the Adams-Onís Treaty?

_____

3. **Defining** What was the rendezvous of Mountain Men?

_____

4. **Identifying** Who were Dr. Marcus Whitman and his wife Narcissa?

_____

_____

5. **Defining** Who were emigrants?

_____

6. **Analyzing** How did popular thinking about the mission of the United States change in the 1800s?

_____

_____

7. **Naming** What was John O'Sullivan's name for the idea that the country was destined by God to possess the entire continent?

_____

8. **Explaining** What did the slogan "Fifty-Four Forty or Fight" mean?

_____

_____

67

Guided Reading Activity

Manifest Destiny

Independence for Texas

Reading Tip

Make a list of questions that you have about this section that you do not understand. Present these questions to your teacher and to the class for help.

Outlining   DIRECTIONS: Read the section and complete the outline below.

I. A Clash of Cultures

   A. Most of the residents in Texas were Mexicans called _____.

   B. _____ obtained land grants in Texas and recruited settlers.

   C. _____ organized a colony in Texas and became a leader among American settlers there.

   D. Mexico discouraged trade between Texas and the United States through a(n) _____ on imported goods.

   E. _____ declared himself dictator of Mexico.

II. The Struggle for Independence

   A. Davy Crockett, Jim Bowie, and William B. Travis led a small group of Americans who were defeated by Mexicans at the _____.

   B. Texas settlers declared independence in 1836 and established a(n) _____.

   C. _____ was named commander in chief of the Texas forces.

   D. Texans who had surrendered were executed on Santa Anna's orders at the "_____ Massacre."

   E. The Texans soundly defeated the Mexicans under Santa Anna at the battle of _____.

   F. A Texas delegation asked the United States to _____ Texas.

   G. During the 1844 presidential campaign, the winning candidate, _____, supported Texas statehood.

Guided Reading Activity

Manifest Destiny

War With Mexico

Reading Tip Write the key words of the section on the front of note cards and their definitions on the back. Study the cards as you study the chapter.

Filling in the Blanks   DIRECTIONS: Read the section and fill in the blanks using the words in the box. Some words might not be used.

Californios	Guadalupe Hidalgo	James K. Polk
ranchos	New Mexico	Rio Grande
Mexican Cession	Gadsden Purchase	Bear Flag
Santa Fe Trail	John C. Frémont	California
Stephen Watts Kearny	Zachary Taylor	Mexico City

The **(1)** _____ Territory was inherited by Mexico from Spain. American trader William Becknell established the **(2)** _____ as the major route into the territory.

Mexico also owned **(3)** _____, where settlers established huge estates called

(4) _____.

President **(5)** _____ wanted to gain these lands from Mexico through war. He ordered General **(6)** _____ to enter disputed land to provoke a Mexican attack, which resulted in a declaration of war.

General **(7)** _____ captured Santa Fe while **(8)** _____ set out to conquer California. This angered the **(9)** _____, Mexicans who lived in the newly proclaimed **(10)** _____ Republic. Their revolt was put down, and California was under full American control.

General Winfield Scott captured **(11)** _____, and the Mexican government surrendered. In the Treaty of **(12)** _____, Mexico gave up Texas and agreed to the

(13) _____ as the border between them. The United States gained California and New Mexico through the **(14)** _____.

Guided Reading Activity

Manifest Destiny

California and Utah

Reading Tip
After you have read a section, try to summarize each section of text under each head in one or two sentences.

Reading for Accuracy   DIRECTIONS: Use your textbook to decide if a statement is true or false. Write **T** or **F** in the blank. If a statement is false, rewrite it to make it true.

_____ 1. Because gold was discovered in California in 1848, people who went there to seek gold were called forty-eighters.

_____

_____ 2. New communities called boomtowns sprang up almost overnight.

_____

_____ 3. Most miners found gold and achieved lasting wealth.

_____

_____ 4. Because mining towns were typically lawless, citizens formed groups called vigilantes to protect themselves.

_____

_____ 5. California's constitution permitted slavery.

_____

_____ 6. The founder of the Mormon Church was Brigham Young.

_____

_____ 7. Joseph Smith wanted to build an ideal society where property would be held in common.

_____

_____ 8. The destination of the Mormon migration westward was the Great Salt Lake.

_____

North and South

Copyright © Glencoe/McGraw-Hill, a division of The McGraw-Hill Companies, Inc.

Content Vocabulary Activity

North and South

Defining DIRECTIONS: Select a term that matches each definition below. Write the correct term in the space provided.

clipper ship	discrimination	tenant farmer
telegraph	famine	overseer
Morse code	nativist	spiritual
trade union	cotton gin	slave codes
strike	capital	literacy
prejudice	yeoman	

1. *Definition:* money used to invest in businesses

Term: _____

2. *Definition:* a refusal to work in order to put pressure on employers

Term: _____

3. *Definition:* a person who either rented or worked on other people's land

Term: _____

4. *Definition:* a series of dots and dashes that represent the letters of the alphabet

Term: _____

5. *Definition:* the unfair treatment of a group

Term: _____

6. *Definition:* an African American religious folk song

Term: _____

7. *Definition:* a ship with a sleek hull and tall sail

Term: _____

8. *Definition:* an extreme shortage of food

Term: _____

9. *Definition:* a farmer who did not own enslaved workers

Term: _____

Copyright © Glencoe/McGraw-Hill, a division of The McGraw-Hill Companies, Inc.

Content Vocabulary Activity (continued)

10. *Definition:* a machine invented by Eli Whitney that could remove seeds from fibers

    Term: _____

11. *Definition:* a plantation manager

    Term: _____

12. *Definition:* a device that transmitted messages through electrical signals

    Term: _____

13. *Definition:* a person who was opposed to immigration

    Term: _____

14. *Definition:* the ability of people to read and write

    Term: _____

15. *Definition:* an organization of workers with the same type of skill

    Term: _____

16. *Definition:* laws in the Southern states that controlled enslaved people

    Term: _____

17. *Definition:* an unfair opinion that is not based on facts

    Term: _____

Copyright © Glencoe/McGraw-Hill, a division of The McGraw-Hill Companies, Inc.

Academic Vocabulary Activity

North and South

Academic Words in This Chapter

innovation	community	consequence
transform	license	legal

A. Word Meaning Activity: Matching Definitions

Directions: Match the academic words in Column A to their definitions in Column B.

Column A

_____ **1.** innovation

_____ **2.** transform

_____ **3.** community

_____ **4.** license

_____ **5.** consequence

_____ **6.** legal

Column B

A. permission granted by an authority

B. allowed by law

C. to change

D. the result of an action

E. new ideas or methods

F. a group of people living in a particular area

Academic Vocabulary Activity (continued)

B. Word Usage Activity: Understanding Words With Multiple Meanings

Directions: Some words like *innovate* have different meanings depending on the form used. Match the definitions to the sentences below. Write the correct letter in the spaces provided.

a. (v.) to do something in a new way

b. (n.) someone who does things in new ways

c. (adj.) a new idea or method

_____ **1.** Her main job responsibility is to develop <u>innovative</u> ideas for changing the company's Web site.

_____ **2.** The microwave was an <u>innovational</u> product when it was invented.

_____ **3.** He is a real <u>innovator</u> and always has new ideas.

Primary Source Readings

North and South

Northern Oppression

Interpreting the Source

Because of slavery, we usually link oppression of African Americans with the pre–Civil War South. However, African Americans also experienced racism in the North, especially during riots when whites terrorized blacks. One riot took place in Philadelphia in August 1842. Several people were killed, with many more injured. Riots like this one often happened during times of economic depression. The letter below, written by an anonymous African American to the abolitionist paper the *Liberator*, shows how the spirits of African Americans suffered during the riot.

Guided Reading

As you read, think about how the riot affected the author's moods and feelings.

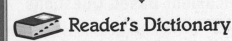

📖 Reader's Dictionary

interrogatories: questions

wantonness: cruel or immoral behavior

tendril: threadlike growth that certain plants, such as grapes, use for support

pall: a covering that darkens

I am every way disqualified for making proper answers to your **interrogatories** in reference to one of the most ferocious and bloody-spirited mobs that ever cursed a *Christian* community. I know not where to begin, nor where nor how to end, in a detail of the **wantonness,** brutality and murderous spirit of the actors in the late riots; nor of the apathy and inhumanity of the whole community, in regard to the matter. Press, church, magistrates, clergymen and devils are against us. The measure of our suffering is full.

"Man's inhumanity to man," indeed makes countless millions mourn. From the most painful and minute investigation into the feelings, views and acts of this community, in regard to us, I am convinced of our utter and complete nothingness in public estimation. I feel that my life, and those **tendrils** of my heart, dearer than life to me, would find no change in death, but a glorious riddance of life, weighed down and crushed by a despotism whose sway makes hell of earth—we the *tormented*, our persecutors the *tormentors*.

But I must stop. I am sick, miserably sick. Every thing around me is as dark as the grave. Here and there, the bright countenance of a true friend is to be seen. Save that, nothing redeeming, nothing hopeful. Despair, as black as the **pall** of death, hangs over us, and the bloody *will* is in the heart of the community to destroy us.

Name_____ Date_____ Class_____

 Primary Source Readings (continued)

(continued)

To attempt to reply to your letter, now, is impracticable.
"I have no feeling—Scarce conscious is what I wish." Yet never forget my
gratitude to you, and all the dear, true and faithful friends in the sacred cause
of human freedom.

Source: *A Documentary History of the Negro People in the United States.* New York: The Citadel Press, 1951.

DBQ Document-Based Questions

Directions: Answer the questions below in the spaces provided.

1. **Paraphrasing** What is the author's opinion about how the general public views African Americans?

   _____

   _____

2. **Evaluating** What would death mean to the author at this point in his life?

   _____

   _____

3. **Explaining** Why does the author stop writing his letter?

   _____

   _____

4. **Making Inferences** Why does the author put "Christian" in italics at the beginning of his letter?

   _____

   _____

5. **Formulating questions** Write a question that you would ask the writer of this passage.

   _____

   _____

78

Writing Skills Activity

North and South

Anticipating and Answering Reader Concerns

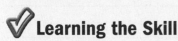 **Learning the Skill**

"I want to get a job when I turn 16." When trying to persuade others, you need to think ahead to what concerns or arguments they may have regarding your position. You need to have answers ready for others' questions. If you tell your parents you want to get a job, you can anticipate that your parents will have questions about how you intend to keep your grades up or continue your extracurricular activities. They might want to know how you plan to get to and from your job. You may tell them you intend to look for a job located on a bus line or within walking distance of your home. You might assure them you are looking for a part-time job that is no more than 15 hours a week to allow you time for homework.

When you are writing a persuasive composition, you will want to antici-pate the questions your readers might have and assemble your evidence to win them over. Follow these steps to address concerns when writing a composition:

- State and summarize your position on a topic.
- Think of the concerns your readers may have regarding your position.
- Review your position from the perspectives of those who are against the position and those who would want further information or clarification.
- Organize these concerns logically, and respond to them using details, rea-sons, and examples.

Practicing the Skill

Directions: Imagine you are living in the South in the 1800s. You are in favor of mandatory public education. List two arguments from those who disagree with you that you believe you will need to address.

Your position:

Children should go to school because they will learn how to be good citizens. They will also gain general knowledge that will help them in the future and learn how to read and write.

Example of argument against your position:

Parents can teach their children better than the schools.

Writing Skills Activity (continued)

Additional arguments against your position:

1. _____

_____

2. _____

_____

✔ Applying the Skill

Directions: Imagine you are a member of a trade union in the mid-1830s. You and your co-workers are preparing to go on strike. Present your position on why going on strike is important in a letter to a local newspaper. Give reasons to support your position. Consider the position of your employer and address these concerns, as well.

_____

_____

_____

_____

_____

_____

_____

_____

_____

_____

_____

_____

_____

_____

Self-Assessment Checklist

Assess your argument using the checklist below:

☐ I stated and summarized my position.

☐ I thought of concerns that readers may have.

☐ I reviewed my position from their perspective.

☐ I responded to concerns using details, reasons, and examples.

☐ I organized concerns logically.

Social Studies Skills Activity

North and South

Interpreting Data in Tables

 Learning the Skill

Tables are often created to organize data. After studying the data from various sources, tables are made to allow you to see trends or patterns. For example, a table may show population trends over a period of time. Information in a table may also compare different types of data.

   To interpret the data in a table, follow these steps:
- Read the title of the table to determine its subject.
- Read each column heading to see what categories are being compared.
- Study the data from the top down in each column and across rows.
- Identify relationships and draw conclusions.

Practicing the Skill

Directions: Read the paragraph below, and then complete the table that follows with information you read in the paragraph and in your textbook. Make sure to specify how each item produced was used.

> During the mid-1800s, women working in Northern industries dealt with discrimination, lower pay than men, and exclusion from unions. Industries that employed women included: textile, metal, machinery, and leather. Some of the products produced were guns, shoes, sewing machines, agricultural machinery, clothing, and watches.

Women in Industry—Mid-1800s		
Industry	Product Made	Product Usage
Textile Industry		
Metal Industry		
Machinery Industry		
Leather Industry		

Social Studies Skills Activity (continued)

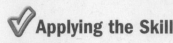 ### Applying the Skill

Directions: Women's jobs in today's workforce are quite different from the mid-1800s. In 2006 there were approximately 67 million women working in the United States. Study the table below, and then answer the questions that follow.

Distribution of Female American Workers, 2006		
Industry	**Percentage of Workforce**	**Total Workforce (approximately 67 million)**
Management, professional, and related occupations	38%	25,460,000
Sales and office	34%	22,780,000
Service	20%	13,400,000
Production, transportation, and material moving	6%	4,020,000
Natural resources, construction, and maintenance	1%	670,000

Source: U.S. Department of Labor, Bureau of Labor Statistics, 2006.

1. **Identifying** What is the subject of the table?

_____

_____

2. **Calculating** Approximately how many women worked in the service industry in 2006? What was the percentage of the total workforce?

_____

_____

3. **Contrasting** Refer to the "Women in Industry—Mid-1800s" table you just completed and the one above. On a separate sheet of paper, write a paragraph explaining some of the statistical differences you found between the two tables.

Self-Assessment Checklist

Assess your paragraphs using the checklist below:

☐ I wrote a paragraph about women in industry during the mid-1800s and today.

☐ I wrote a paragraph that contrasted the data in the tables.

☐ I wrote a well-composed paragraph using correct grammar, punctuation, and spelling.

Differentiated Instruction Activity
North and South

Toys of the Old South

During the 1800s, children in the South played with many kinds of toys. Unlike toys of today, these play items were usually not made in factories or sold in stores. Instead, they were made by hand from natural products, such as rags, string, gourds, and wood, found at home or in fields and woods. In the early

South, Native Americans had crafted dolls from corn cobs and husks and carved small replicas of tools and weapons from wood. They later shared their methods of making toys with European and African settlers. Meanwhile, settlers brought toys and games from their homelands. Children from wealthy families living in towns or on plantations enjoyed fancy dolls, tea sets, and wooden soldiers brought from Europe. Most children, however, lived and worked on small family farms and could not afford these expensive toys.

During leisure time, they played with homemade balls, tops, blocks, puzzles, jump ropes, and hoops. On Sundays, children in religious families could play only with toys based on Bible stories. One was the Noah's Ark toy, a carved wooden boat house filled with painted figures of Noah, his family, and animals.

Pull toys especially fascinated children. The most popular was the "peg top," a single carved piece of wood set in motion by a wound string. Many children played a game called "peg in the ring," in which tops were spun in circles. If one player's top bumped into another, that player could keep the other person's top. Another popular pull toy was the whirligig, which spun around when someone pulled its string.

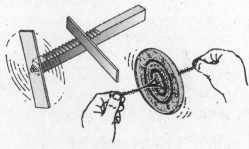

By the late 1850s, commercial toy makers in major cities were producing many different kinds of toys, including wooden rocking horses, tin soldiers, horses, and animals. As the Civil War neared, America's toy industry was prospering. It would continue to grow in the years ahead as the South—and the nation as a whole—became more urban and industrialized.

Source: Sharon A. Sharp, "Folklife: Toys." In *Encyclopedia of Southern Culture*, vol 2. New York: Anchor Books, 1991.

Directions: Use the information from the text above and your textbook to answer the following questions on a separate sheet of paper.

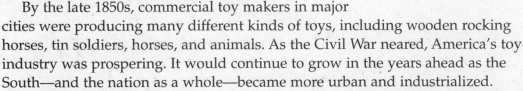

1. **Identifying** What local materials did Southern settlers use to make toys?

2. **Making Inferences** Why were children in the Old South often allowed to play only with biblically based toys on Sundays?

Copyright © Glencoe/McGraw-Hill, a division of The McGraw-Hill Companies, Inc.

Differentiated Instruction Activity (continued)

Teaching Strategies for Different Learning Styles

The following activities are ways the basic lesson can be modified to accommodate students' different learning styles.

English Language Learner (ELL)

Have students identify the names of all of the toys mentioned in the article. Then invite them to tell the class about folk toys from their own cultures.

Gifted and Talented

How do children's playthings reflect the culture in which the children live? What will historians conclude about our own times, based on the things adults give their children to play with? Assign students to write about this topic in a three- to four-page paper, using the article, their own research, and their own experiences to support their arguments.

Verbal/Linguistic; Intrapersonal

Ask students to use the Internet to find how many toys in the article can still be purchased today. Direct them to online craft stores or cybershops specializing in "folk" items. Have students record the prices of each toy. Then have them write one or two pages about why such "old-fashioned" toys are still made and why people still want them.

Logical/Mathematical

Venn diagrams help students categorize and classify information by comparing and/or contrasting two or more items. Ask students to find out more about one of the toys described in the article using the library media center or Internet resources. Also have them identify their own favorite childhood toy. Then have them draw a Venn diagram on a piece of paper. One circle should have the name of the "old-fashioned" toy they researched; the other should have the title of their own favorite toy. Students should then write information about each in the respective circle. Qualities that both toys share should be written into the overlapping area.

Visual/Spatial; Interpersonal

Assign pairs of students the task of creating a television commercial or an advertisement for one of the toys described in the article. Teams can use whatever medium they choose to create their ads. Students should present their commercials or explain their ads to the class.

Auditory/Musical

Children's games are frequently accompanied by songs or chants. Have students research several examples of game songs, counting-out rhymes, nursery rhymes, and fingerplay songs from the mid-1800s and share them with the class. Briefly discuss the characteristics of the songs.

Kinesthetic

Ask students to make one of the toys described in the article. (Directions for making such toys are easily found online.) Invite selected students to demonstrate the toys to the class, explaining how they were made and how they were used.

Naturalist

Most of the toys described in the article were made from items people found in their environment. Instruct students to research the types of toys made by people in different regions of North America (e.g., the Great Plains, the Pacific Northwest, the Southwest) in the early to mid-1800s. Students should focus their research on the ways people used natural materials that were readily at hand. They should present their findings in a three-page paper.

Critical Thinking Skills Activity

North and South

Drawing Conclusions

 Learning the Skill

When you read a book or an article, you may need to look beyond what is
actually written on the page to fully understand its meaning. By considering
the facts presented and using your own knowledge, you can draw conclusions
that allow you to understand more than what is actually stated on the page.

 Practicing the Skill

Directions: The excerpt below is from an interview with 80-year-old Clayton
Holbert, a formerly enslaved African American. Read the excerpt, and then
answer the questions that follow.

> My name is Clayton Holbert, and I am an ex-slave. . . . My master's name was Pleasant "Ples"
> Holbert. My master had . . . around one hundred slaves. . . . They always had a man in the field to teach
> the small boys to work, and I was one of the boys. I was learning to plant corn, etc. My father, brother
> and uncle went to war on the Union side. We raised corn, barley, and cotton, and produced all of our
> living on the plantation. There was no such thing as going to town to buy things. . . . For our meat we
> used to kill . . . hogs. . . . We also made our own sorghum, dried our own fruits. . . . I was never sold. I
> always had just one master. When slave owners died, if they had no near relatives to inherit their
> property, they would "Will" the slaves their freedom. . . . My grandmother and my mother were both freed
> like this, but [dishonest] . . . traders captured them [again] . . . and they took them just like they would
> animals, and sold them, that was how "Ples" Holbert got my mother. My grandmother was sent to Texas.
> My mother . . . never saw her again. . . . After the war was over . . . it left my mother alone. . . . [She] got
> her freedom, she and me, I was seven or eight years old, and my brother was fourteen, and my sister
> was about sixteen. . . . [My] master said that we could stay and work for him a year, and then we also
> stayed there the following year, and he paid us the second year.

Source: *The American Slave*, Clayton Holbert, Ottawa, Kansas, interviewed by Leta Gray.

1. **Drawing Conclusions** How long was Clayton Holbert enslaved? How long
   was he free? How did you come to your conclusions?

   _____

   _____

2. **Speculating** How do you think Clayton Holbert got his last name?

   _____

   _____

Critical Thinking Skills Activity (continued)

3. **Determining Cause and Effect** In what ways did the Civil War affect Clayton Holbert's family?

_____

_____

4. **Determining Cause and Effect** What effect did slavery have on Clayton Holbert's family?

_____

_____

✓ Applying the Skill

Directions: Use the passage about Clayton Holbert to answer the following questions. Circle the letter of the correct answer.

1. How does the passage suggest how Holbert felt about having been enslaved?
   A. He thought it was brutal.
   B. His experience was not brutal, but he regretted the effects on his loved ones.
   C. He wished he were still enslaved.
   D. He did not mind being enslaved because he liked his owner.

2. What did Clayton Holbert's family do after the Civil War?
   A. They immediately bought their own farm.
   B. They left right away to join family up north.
   C. They stayed on the plantation where they had been enslaved for two more years.
   D. They never left the plantation where they had been enslaved.

3. Which of the jobs below would Clayton Holbert be prepared to do?
   A. farmer
   B. soldier
   C. blacksmith
   D. teacher

Geography and History Activity

North and South

Changing the Landscape for Industry

Several geographic factors nurtured the development of the Industrial Revolution in New England beginning around 1800. The New England states had many rushing rivers and streams that could provide the water-power needed to run factory machinery. Nearby, Pennsylvania's coal, iron, and other natural resources needed for industry were easily accessible. Also, New England had several port cities. Through these ports, shipments of raw cotton from the South could be taken in, and finished cloth products could be sent out. Several industrial cities in New England sprang up to take advantage of these natural geographic features. Lowell, Massachusetts, was the first planned industrial city in America.

Natural Features

Investors looking for places to build textile mills were attracted to a site near where the Merrimack River joins with the Concord River. Here, at Pawtucket Falls, the Merrimack drops more than 30 feet in less than a mile. The falls create a continuous flow of energy that could be harnessed to power machinery. The city of Lowell was founded on this site in 1821.

Human Modifications

The natural features of the site chosen for Lowell were outstanding. Yet, it was not long before mill owners began to modify the landscape to make those natural features even more useful and accessible. Six miles of canals were built on two levels to bring waterpower to 40 mill sites in Lowell. Also, to make more efficient use of the Merrimack River, mill owners dammed it. They held water in the dam overnight for the next day's factory use. Lowell mill owners also purchased water rights in New Hampshire. The owners stored the water in lakes in the spring and released it into the Merrimack during the dry seasons of summer and fall.

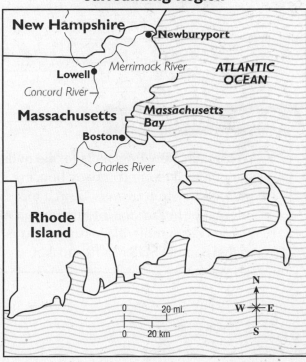

Lowell, Massachusetts, and Surrounding Region

Geography and History Activity (continued)

✓ Applying Geography to History

Directions: Answer the following questions in the spaces provided.

1. Stating What natural features most attracted investors to the Lowell site?

_____

_____

2. Analyzing Visuals What bodies of water were accessible to the Lowell mills?

_____

_____

3. Discussing What three modifications did Lowell mill owners make to the landscape?

_____

_____

_____

4. Predicting How might the environment be affected by the modifications that the Lowell mill owners made?

_____

_____

_____

5. Drawing Conclusions How might raw materials needed for the manufacture of finished textile goods have been transported to Lowell?

_____

_____

_____

GOING FURTHER ▶ ▶▶▶

- Workers in New England's textile mills sometimes lived in company housing provided by mill owners. Search the Internet or library for information about Slatersville, a mill village run by industrialist Samuel Slater in Pawtucket, Rhode Island. What was it like to live there? What was it like to work in the mills? Write a brief report and include your opinion about whether or not the Slatersville mill village was a good place for families to live.

Linking Past and Present Activity

North and South

From Hand Tools to Tractors

THEN In the early 1800s, an agricultural revolution changed farming forever. New horse-drawn machines substituted animal power for hand labor. In a matter of hours, farmers completed work that once took days.

In 1831 Cyrus McCormick manufactured a reaper, which made harvesting crops much easier and faster. A divider separated and cut standing grain. A spinning reel loaded the grain onto a rear platform. Workers raked this grain onto the ground and bundled it.

The combine harvester performed the operations of a reaper and a thresher—a machine that separates seeds from plants and removes their hulls. Using these machines, farmers cultivated larger plots of land. McCormick's reaper and other farm machines invented in the 1800s helped turn the United States into an agricultural giant.

NOW By the 1920s, manufacturers had adapted automobile technology for agricultural use. Internal combustion engines now powered farm machines. Crop production increased to levels not believed possible in the mid-1800s. Today's American farms lead the world in crop production. They have earned the Midwest the nickname "Breadbasket of the World."

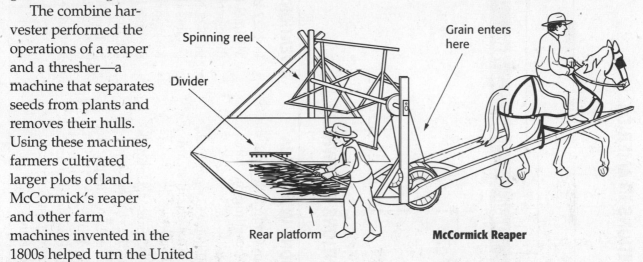

Spinning reel

Divider

Grain enters here

Rear platform

McCormick Reaper

Directions: Answer the questions below on a separate sheet of paper.

1. **Determining Cause and Effect** How did the farm machines introduced in the 1830s change farming?

2. **Explaining** What was the function of the divider on the McCormick reaper?

3. **Speculating** What do you think life on an American farm in the late 1800s would have been like if no one had invented the reaper?

4. **Drawing Conclusions** Why do you think the *combine* harvester was given that name?

5. **Making Inferences** Why do manufacturers often describe engines in terms of *horsepower*?

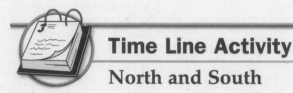

Time Line Activity

North and South

Inventions in the Early 1800s (1822–1861)

Directions: Use the following information about the technological advances in the early to mid-1800s to create a time line.

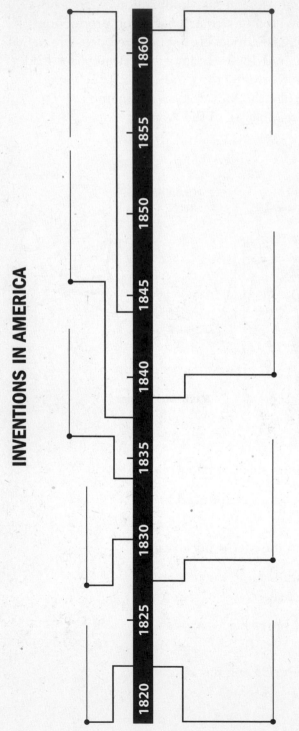

INVENTIONS ELSEWHERE

INVENTIONS ELSEWHERE

- In 1822 British scientist Michael Faraday develops the electric motor.
- In 1827 Nicephore Niepce obtains the first camera image.
- Kirkpatrick MacMillan, a Scottish blacksmith, invents the first useful bicycle in 1839.
- In 1861 Johann Philipp Reis designs sound-transmitting instruments in Germany.

INVENTIONS IN AMERICA

- William Church designs the first typesetting machine in 1822.
- In 1830 Peter Cooper builds the first American steam locomotive.
- In 1834 Cyrus McCormick patents the reaper.
- John Deere invents the steel plow in 1837.
- Samuel F.B. Morse demonstrates the first practical telegraph in 1844.

Background

The Industrial Revolution in the United States began around 1800. It created demands for revolutionary advances in transportation, communications, agriculture, and industry. Inventors in the United States met those demands. New technology was being developed in other countries during this same time period. Some of these countries had already experienced an industrial revolution.

Name_____ Date_____ Class_____

School-to-Home Connection Activity

North and South

What Do You Know?

Directions: Ask each other the following questions to see how much you know about the similarities and differences between the Northern and Southern states.*

Student: How did clipper ships get their name?

Partner's answer:

Student's answer:

Partner: Why did skilled workers in New York City strike in the 1830s?

Student: How did the invention of the cotton gin revolutionize cotton production?

Partner's answer:

Student's answer:

Partner: Why was it a crime for enslaved people to read or write?

*With your student, find answers to these questions in the student textbook.

🏠 School-to-Home Connection Activity (continued)

Understanding the Essential Questions

Directions: Rewrite each Essential Question as a statement. Then use your textbook to help you write details that support your statement in the graphic organizer provided.

Section 1 What innovations in industry, travel, and communications changed the lives of Americans in the 1800s?

Statement: _____

Innovations in Industry	Innovations in Travel	Innovations in Communications

Section 2 How did immigration have an impact on cities, industry, and culture in the North?

Statement: _____

Immigration Impact	⇨	On cities:
		On industry:
		On culture:

Section 3 How did the South's industry and economy differ from the industry and economy of the North?

Statement: _____

	Type of Economy	Type of Labor	Rate of Industrial Growth
South			
North			

Section 4 How did unique elements of culture develop among enslaved African Americans in the South?

Statement: _____

92

Name_____ Date_____ Class_____

Reteaching Activity

North and South

In the mid-1800s, North and South were developing along different paths. While industrialization was sweeping the North, cotton was becoming king in the South. Different cultures were emerging in the two regions as well. Differences between North and South would eventually lead to civil war.

Determining Cause and Effect   DIRECTIONS: Each phrase below describes a factor in either economic or cultural development of different regions. Write the phrases in the appropriate spaces in the diagrams.

cotton gin	unions	reliance on slave labor
slave codes	nativism	growth of factories
steamboats	railroads	worker specialization
lower prices	immigration	economy based on agriculture

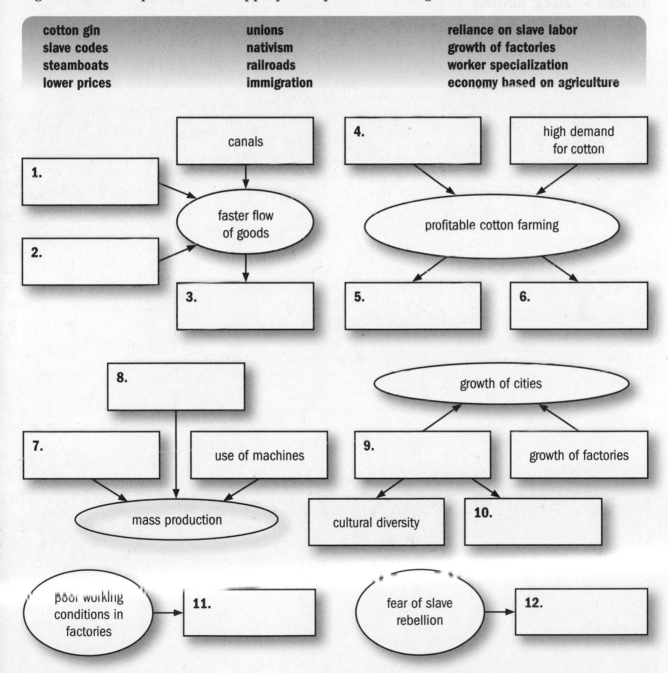

Section Resources

Name_____ Date_____ Class_____

Guided Reading Activity

North and South

The North's Economy

Reading Tip   Take notes as you read, and be sure to go back to those notes and organize them. You will remember more when the information is organized.

Answering Questions   DIRECTIONS: As you read the section, answer the questions below.

1. **Summarizing** What were the three phases of industrialization in the North?

_____

_____

2. **Identifying** What invention helped workers produce clothing on a large scale and who was the inventor?

_____

3. **Naming** Who designed and built the first American steam locomotive and what was it called?

_____

4. **Explaining** How did canals and railways transform trade in the nation's interior?

_____

_____

5. **Defining** What is Morse code and what is it used for?

_____

6. **Identifying** What three inventions changed farming methods and encouraged greater cultivation in the Midwest?

_____

7. **Determining Cause and Effect** What was the impact of McCormick's reaper on the Midwestern economy?

_____

_____

Guided Reading Activity
North and South

The North's People

Reading Tip

After reading a long paragraph or section, pause to restate or summarize it in your head or on paper what you have just read.

Filling in the Blanks   DIRECTIONS: Use your textbook to fill in the blanks using the words in the box. Some words may not be used.

working hours	Irish	prejudice
Sarah G. Bagley	strikes	Nativists
Know-Nothing	anti-Catholic	Germany
trade unions	discrimination	wages
British	famine	Macon B. Allen

As the factory system developed in the North, working conditions worsened. In response, skilled workers formed **(1)** _____ and sometimes staged **(2)** _____ in order to put pressure on employers. Workers wanted to receive higher **(3)** _____ and to limit their **(4)** _____.

Even though slavery had largely disappeared from the North, African Americans faced racial **(5)** _____ and **(6)** _____ in their everyday lives. Women workers also faced hardships and some, including Massachusetts weaver **(7)** _____, organized for labor reform.

Immigrants provided a large labor force for Northern factories. **(8)** _____ immigrants, having left their homeland because of **(9)** _____, worked on railroads and took low-paying factory jobs. Immigrants from **(10)** _____ were typically more prosperous, buying farms and starting businesses. However, anti-immigrant prejudice rose during this time. **(11)** _____ feared that the newcomers were changing the country's character too much. A new political party, nicknamed the **(12)** _____ Party, called for stricter citizenship laws.

Section

Guided Reading Activity

North and South

Southern Cotton Kingdom

Reading Tip
Turn the chapter headings and subheadings in the section into questions.
Write these questions down. Try to answer these questions as you study for the quiz or test.

Outlining   DIRECTIONS: Read the section and complete the outline below.

I. Rise of the Cotton Kingdom

    A. The economy of the South depended on _____.

    B. The _____ revolutionized cotton production.

    C. The _____ South produced tobacco while the

        _____ South depended upon cotton as its major crop.

    D. The value of _____ increased because they were central to
        the production of cotton and sugar.

II. Industry in the South

    A. A major obstacle to Southern industry was the lack of

        _____ to invest in businesses.

    B. Some Southerners believed that the South depended too much on the

        _____ for manufactured goods.

    C. One of the nation's leading iron producers was the _____
        located in Virginia.

    D. Natural _____ were used to transport goods in the South.

    E. The South had fewer _____ than the North, which
        resulted in the slower growth of cities.

Guided Reading Activity

North and South

The South's People

Reading Tip

After you have read a section, stop and ask yourself: "What is the purpose of this material?" If you cannot answer that question, go back and reread to find the answer.

Reading for Accuracy   **DIRECTIONS:** Use your textbook to decide if a statement is true or false. Write **T** or **F** in the blank. If a statement is false, rewrite it to make it true.

_____ 1. Most white Southerners were wealthy planters with enslaved workers.

   _____

_____ 2. Yeomen worked as tenant farmers on landlords' estates.

   _____

_____ 3. Plantation owners measured their wealth partly by the number of enslaved people they owned.

   _____

_____ 4. Overseers were in charge of plantation households.

   _____

_____ 5. Enslaved families were not protected by American laws in the early 1800s.

   _____

_____ 6. When Congress outlawed the slave trade in 1808, slavery became illegal in the South.

   _____

_____ 7. Slave codes prohibited large assemblies of enslaved people.

   _____

_____ 8. The Underground Railroad was a network of safe houses for enslaved people who escaped.

   _____

The Age of Reform

Content Vocabulary Activity

The Age of Reform

Identifying   **DIRECTIONS:** Select a term to answer each question below.

revival	transcendentalists	Underground Railroad
utopia	civil disobedience	suffrage
temperance	abolitionist	coeducation
normal school		

1. Where could high school graduates go for further education to become

   teachers? _____

2. What was the name of the route traveled by African Americans who

   were trying to escape slavery in the South? _____

3. The teaching of males and females together is called what?

   _____

4. People in the early 1800s traveled great distances to hear preachers
   speak and to pray, sing, weep, and shout at what type of religious

   meeting? _____

5. What is the term used to describe the practice of refusing to obey laws

   that are considered unjust? _____

6. The right to vote is called what? _____

7. What is a community that is based on a vision of a perfect society?

   _____

8. What is the term used to describe a reformer who worked to end

   slavery? _____

Copyright © Glencoe/McGraw-Hill, a division of The McGraw-Hill Companies, Inc.

Content Vocabulary Activity (continued)

9. The idea of drinking little or no alcohol in order to protect society is

   called what? _____

10. Who were the thinkers and writers that stressed the relationship
    between humans and nature and the importance of the individual

    conscience? _____

Academic Vocabulary Activity
The Age of Reform

Academic Words in this Chapter

lecture	medical	ministry
route	capable	

A. Word Meaning Activity: Identifying Synonyms and Antonyms

Directions: *Synonyms* are words with similar meanings, and *antonyms* are words with opposite meanings. Determine whether the following pairs of words or phrases are synonyms or antonyms. Place an "S" in the blank if the words are synonyms and an "A" in the blank if they are antonyms.

1. _____ lecture—speech

2. _____ route—passage

3. _____ medical—health

4. _____ capable—incompetent

5. _____ ministry—Christian service

B. Word Usage Activity: Using Words in Context

Directions: Write one vocabulary word from the box above on each line to complete the sentences.

1. Some pioneering women felt they were _____ of learning subjects such as science and math, which were previously thought of as only male topics of study.

2. Southerners argued that enslaved people benefited by not having to pay for food, clothing, or _____ care.

3. He listened to the _____ and read the pamphlet warning him of the dangers of liquor.

4. A few determined women eventually broke into male-dominated professions such as medicine and the _____.

5. The group of enslaved people followed the conductor along the escape _____ toward the North and freedom.

Academic Vocabulary Activity (continued)

C. Word Family Activity: Completing a Word Chart

DIRECTIONS: A *noun* is a word that names a person, a place, a thing, or an idea. Examples include *president, Chicago, army,* and *slavery.* A *verb* is a word that is used to describe an action, an experience, or a state of being. Examples include *govern, attempt,* and *seem.* An *adjective* is a word used to describe a noun. Examples include *interesting, numeric,* and *comical.* Some words have more than one form. Place a check mark (√) in the appropriate column.

Words	Noun	Verb	Adjective
1. lecture			
2. lecturing			
3. route			
4. routing			
5. medical			
6. medicine			
7. medic			
8. capable			
9. capability			
10. minister			
11. ministry			

Primary Source Readings

The Age of Reform

Women's Wrongs

Interpreting the Source

Lucretia Mott and Elizabeth Cady Stanton were two leading women's rights advocates of the 1800s. Like many other advocates of their day, they were also active abolitionists, yet they could not participate in the 1840 World Anti-Slavery Convention in London because they were women. Angered at such treatment and inspired by the Declaration of Independence and the ideals of Jacksonian democracy, Mott and Stanton organized the first women's rights convention in Seneca Falls, New York, in 1848. Two years later, another convention took place in Salem, Ohio. J. Elizabeth Jones of Salem, editor of the *Anti-Slavery Bugle* and an ardent supporter of women's rights, delivered the convention's major address. Excerpts appear below.

Guided Reading

As you read, identify whom Jones blames for the lack of women's rights.

 Reader's Dictionary

arrogating: claiming without justification
degrade: changing to a less-respected state
passive: not resisting
usurpations: unlawful seizing of power

There is not, perhaps, in the wide field of reform, any one subject so difficult to discuss as that of Woman's Rights. I use the term "Woman's Rights," because it is a technical phrase. I like not the expression. It is not Woman's *Rights* of which I design to speak, but of Woman's *Wrongs*. I shall claim nothing for ourselves because of our sex—I shall demand the recognition of no rights on the ground of our womanhood. In the contest which is now being waged in behalf of the enslaved colored man in this land, I have yet to hear the first word in favor of his rights as a colored man; the great point which is sought to be established is this, that the colored man is a human being, and as such, entitled to the free exercise of all the rights which belong to humanity. And we should demand *our* recognition as equal members of the human family. . . .

But tho' woman has no rights peculiar to her sex—*none* which belong to her because she is a woman; yet she has wrongs, great wrongs, which are peculiar to her—wrongs political, wrongs social, aye, and wrongs religious. . . .

[But woman] appears not before the world as a sufferer. Her very name is associated with happiness and hope, with freedom and love and disabilities under which she labors, we are met with incredulity, perchance with sneers and sarcasm. . . .

. . . I am very far from **arrogating** any degree of perfection for my own sex. Neither do I believe that men are any more to blame for the present **degraded** condition of woman, than the women are themselves. . . . [A]t the present time, there is on the part of a majority of women a **passive** yielding up of all their rights, a desire, I might say, to lose their individuality, and merge their existence

Primary Source Readings (continued)

into that of their husbands. It is feminine to feel dependent, to need protection . . . and have the gallantry and chivalry of man extended to us! We have not acted as though we were rational and accountable beings; we have tried to step aside from the battle-field of life, and rid ourselves of the responsibilities of an individual existence. Under such circumstances, it is no wonder that man has taken the power into his own hands. . . .

I say the fact that woman does not know that she is robbed of her rights, shows the extent of her enslavement; it shows that a long train of abuses and **usurpations** has completed the work of degradation—has blinded her to a sense of justice and of equal rights.

Source: *The Salem, Ohio 1850 Women's Rights Convention Proceedings*, compiled and edited by Robert W. Audretsch. Salem Area Bicentennial Committee and Salem Public Library, 1976.

DBQ Document-Based Questions

Directions: Answer the questions below in the spaces provided.

1. **Discussing** Why does Jones not like the term *Woman's Rights*?

_____

_____

2. **Explaining** What do you think Jones says is the point of the "contest" to free the enslaved African American male?

_____

_____

3. **Identifying** Who does Jones blame for the "present degraded condition of woman"?

_____

_____

4. **Hypothesizing** Why does Jones say some women are blind to their own lack of justice and equal rights?

_____

_____

5. **Interpreting** What do you think Jones means in the statement that women are blind "to a sense of justice and equal rights"?

_____

_____

Writing Skills Activity

The Age of Reform

Analyzing Effects of Literary Works

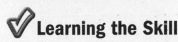 **Learning the Skill**

Often, articles, stories, or books are written to bring about changes in society. The author hopes to make change by encouraging readers to take action. Follow these steps to draw inferences about the effects of a literary work on an audience:

- Read the literary work or selections from the work.
- Identify what the work seems to be saying to the reader. Look for clues in the language used or in the overall tone of the work.
- Who is the intended audience? Do the readers have a different perspective? How do you imagine they will respond to the piece?
- Write your interpretation of the effect of the work, citing examples from the work or influences on others as appropriate.

✓ **Practicing the Skill**

Inspired by Lucretia Mott and Elizabeth Cady Stanton, two leading women's rights advocates, Elizabeth Jones organized a women's rights convention in Salem, Ohio, to take place in April of 1850. The day before, Jones published an announcement of the upcoming event in the Salem *Anti-Slavery Bugle.*

Directions: Read the excerpt from Jones's announcement, and answer the following questions.

> . . . Women of Ohio! We call upon you to come up to this work in the womanly strength, and with womanly energy. While woman is not permitted to attain that expansion of her immortal nature which is her highest privilege, who will withhold any effort which will aid in the elevation of our sex? Don't be discouraged at the possibility of difficulties. Remember that contest with difficulty gives strength. Come and inquire if the position you now occupy is one appointed by wisdom, and designed to secure the best interests of the human race.—Come and let us ascertain what bearing the circumscribed [limited] sphere of Woman has on the great political and social evils that curse and desolate the land. Come! For this cause claims your every talent, your most invincible perseverance. Come in single-heartedness and with a personal self-devotion that will yield every thing to Right, Truth, and Reason. . . .

Source: *The Salem, Ohio 1850 Women's Rights Convention Proceedings,* compiled and edited by Robert W. Audretsch. Salem Area Bicentennial Committee and Salem Public Library, 1976.

1. Explaining For what reason was the convention called?

_____

_____

Writing Skills Activity (continued)

2. Drawing Conclusions Did Jones anticipate any difficulties for women who attend the convention? How do you know?

_____

_____

3. Identifying Points of View What is the overall tone of the piece?

_____

4. Assessing What effect do you think this announcement had on the number of people who attended the convention? Explain your answer.

_____

_____

✓ Applying the Skill

Directions: Henry David Thoreau's 1849 essay *Civil Disobedience* supported the peaceful protest of unfair laws. Read the excerpt below from his essay. On a separate sheet of paper, name two people who have been influenced by Thoreau's ideas, and write a paragraph about how these ideas influenced them.

> Unjust laws exist: shall we be content to obey them, or shall we endeavor to amend them, and obey them until we have succeeded, or shall we transgress [disobey] them at once? Men generally, under such a government as this, think that they ought to wait until they have persuaded the majority to alter them. They think that, if they should resist, the remedy would be worse than the evil. But it is the fault of the government itself that the remedy *is* worse than the evil. *It* makes it worse. Why is it not more apt to anticipate and provide for reform? Why does it not cherish its wise minority? Why does it cry and resist before it is hurt? Why does it not encourage its citizens to be on the alert to point out its faults, and *do* better than it would have them?

Self-Assessment Checklist

Assess your paragraph using the checklist below:

☐ I identified types of actions the author suggests.

☐ I recognized the intended audience.

☐ I anticipated audience response.

☐ I explained how Thoreau's ideas influenced two people.

Chapter

Social Studies Skills Activity

The Age of Reform

Creating a Web Organizer

 Learning the Skill

Web diagrams are used to identify one central idea and organize related information around it. The central idea is written in the middle of the web, and then the broad categories of supporting details are listed in the outer ovals of the diagram.

To create a web diagram, follow these steps:

- Identify the main idea first and place it in the center circle.
- Include at least three broad categories in the outer circles.
- Make sure the broad categories adequately support the main idea.

Practicing the Skill

Directions: During the Second Great Awakening, a group of people called *transcendentalists* made an impact on cultural society. Look at the web diagram below and write the main idea in the center circle. Then answer the questions that follow.

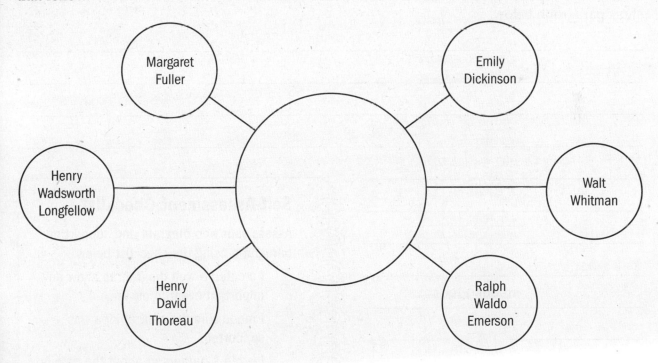

1. **Stating** What is the web diagram about?

_____

_____

Social Studies Skills Activity (continued)

2. **Identifying** Identify a famous poet from the diagram. What did he or she write?

_____

_____

3. **Specifying** What contribution did Margaret Fuller make?

_____

_____

4. **Evaluating** Do you think the transcendentalists had an impact on cultural trends during the Second Great Awakening? Why or why not?

_____

_____

✓ Applying the Skill

Directions: Think of an event that has made a difference in your life. On a separate sheet of paper, create a web diagram about the event. Make sure the outer circles support your central idea. Summarize your web information in a short paragraph below.

_____

_____

_____

_____

_____

_____

_____

_____

_____

_____

Self-Assessment Checklist

Assess your web diagram and supporting paragraph using the checklist below:

☐ I created a web diagram to show an important event in my life.

☐ I made sure the central idea was supported.

☐ I wrote a paragraph about the details of the event in the web diagram.

☐ I checked my paragraph for proper spelling, grammar, and punctuation.

Differentiated Instruction Activity

The Age of Reform

Rules for Husbands and Wives

Mathew Carey (1760–1839) was an Irish-born publisher and editor of various journals in Philadelphia. This excerpt is from his book *Miscellaneous Essays*, published in 1830.

For husbands:

1. A good husband will always regard his wife as his equal; treat her with kindness, respect and attention; and never address her with an air of authority, as if she were, as some husbands appear to regard their wives, a mere housekeeper.

2. He will never interfere in her domestic concerns, hiring servants, &c.

3. He will always keep her liberally supplied with money for furnishing his table in a style proportioned to his means, and for the purchase of dress suitable to her station in life. . . .

4. He will never allow himself to lose his temper towards her, by indifferent cookery, or irregularity in the hours of meals, or any other mismanagement of her servants, knowing the difficulty of making them do their duty.

5. If she have prudence and good sense, he will consult her on all great operations. . . . Many a man has been rescued from destruction by the wise counsels of his wife. Many a foolish husband has most

seriously injured himself and family by the rejection of the advice of his wife, fearing, lest, if he followed it, he would be regarded as ruled by her! A husband can never procure a counsellor more deeply interested in his welfare than his wife. . . .

For wives:

1. A good wife will always receive her husband with smiles . . . and gratefully reciprocate his kindness and attention.

2. She will study to discover the means to gratify his inclinations, in regard to food and cookery; in the management of her family; in her dress, manners and deportment.

3. She will never attempt to rule, or appear to rule her husband. Such conduct degrades husbands—and wives always partake largely of the degradation of their husbands.

4. She will, in every thing reasonable, comply with his wishes—and, as far as possible, anticipate them.

5. She will avoid all altercations or arguments leading to ill-humour—and more especially before company. . . .

Directions: Use the information from the excerpt and your textbook to answer the following questions on a separate sheet of paper.

1. **Evaluating** Do you think most husbands and wives living in the United States in the early 1800s treated each other as suggested by Carey? Why or why not?

2. **Drawing Inferences** At the time of Carey's essay, American women were not permitted to vote. Do you think Carey favored extending the vote to women? Explain your answer.

Differentiated Instruction Activity (continued)

Teaching Strategies for Different Learning Styles

The following activities are ways the basic lesson can be modified to accommodate students' different learning styles.

English Language Learner (ELL)

Have students write down some "rules" followed by husbands and wives in their own cultures. Then have students share those rules with the class.

Special Needs

Prepare paraphrases of Carey's rules, and either give them in written form to students or record them on tape for students to hear. Then have students write or tell which of the rules they think is most important, and why.

Gifted and Talented

Ask students to use the library media center and Internet resources to learn more about the legal rights of American women in the 1800s. They should report their findings in a three- to four-page paper.

Verbal/Linguistic; Intrapersonal

Ask students to write a two-page response to Mathew Carey from the perspective of one of the early pioneers of women's rights, such as Elizabeth Cady Stanton, Mary Lyon, or Susan B. Anthony.

Verbal/Linguistic

Organize the class into three groups. Have one group use the library media center or Internet to learn more about a typical day of a working-class housewife in the early 1800s; the second group will research a middle-class housewife; and the third group will research a wealthy housewife. Students should report their findings in a 5- to 10-minute class presentation.

Logical/Mathematical

Ask students to assign a ranking of 1 (completely disagree) to 5 (completely agree) to each of the points in Carey's essay. Then have them find an average "agreement rating" for both the "husbands' rules" and the "wives' rules." Discuss any differences in class.

Visual/Spatial

Have students create a drawing that illustrates one of Carey's recommendations. Display the work in class, and allow students to guess which are represented.

Kinesthetic; Interpersonal

Organize the class into two groups. Tell them that they are going to write and perform an episode of a television situation comedy entitled "Rules for Husbands and Wives." One group will base its episode on Carey's rules. The other group will formulate its own rules and base its episode on those. Assure students that they can take their episodes in whatever direction they like, as long as the action is plausible and conforms to the appropriate "rules." When they are ready, each group can perform in class.

Below Grade Level

A K-W-L chart taps student knowledge and generates student interest. Have students create a three-column chart titled *Domestic Relations in the 1800s.* Explain that they will fill out the chart by writing what they **K**now about the topic in the first column, what they **W**ant to know in the second, and what they **L**earned in the third. Have students first fill out the **K** and **W** columns. Then ask them to complete the **L** column as they study the chart, read the chapter in their textbooks, and/or conduct their own research.

Critical Thinking Skills Activity

The Age of Reform

Identifying the Main Idea

 Learning the Skill

Identifying the main idea helps you understand historical concepts and why historical events unfold. To identify the main idea in a reading, look for the purpose of the passage and how important details relate to each other.

From the "Declaration of Sentiments," adopted in 1848 at the first American women's rights convention, in Seneca Falls, New York.

. . . The history of mankind is a history of repeated injuries . . . on the part of man toward women . . .

He has never permitted her to exercise her . . . right to the elective franchise [to vote].

He has compelled her to submit to laws, in the formation of which she had no voice . . .

In . . . marriage, she is compelled to promise obedience to her husband, he becoming, to all intents and purposes, her master . . .

He has so framed laws of divorce . . . all cases, going upon the false supposition of the supremacy of man, and giving all power into his hands . . .

He has monopolized nearly all the profitable employments and from those she is permitted to follow, she receives but scanty remuneration [little pay] . . .

He has denied her the facilities for obtaining a thorough education, all colleges being closed against her . . .

He has endeavored . . . to destroy her confidence in her own powers, to lessen her self-respect, and to make her willing to lead a dependent . . . life.

Now . . . because women do feel themselves . . . oppressed, and . . . deprived of their most sacred rights, we insist that they have immediate admission to all rights and privileges which belong to them as citizens of the United States.

. . . We anticipate no small amount of . . . ridicule; but we shall . . . employ agents, circulate tracts, petition the State and National legislatures, and endeavor to enlist the pulpit and the press in our behalf . . .

Source: Elizabeth Cady Stanton, *The Declaration of Sentiments*, Seneca Falls Women's Rights Convention, July 19–20, 1848.

 Practicing the Skill

Directions: Use the passage to answer the following questions.

1. **Identifying Central Issues** What is the main idea of this passage from the Declaration of Sentiments?

_____

_____

Critical Thinking Skills Activity (continued)

2. Identifying Points of View What is the woman's place in the workplace in 1848?

_____

3. Making Inferences What does the author of this passage hope to accomplish for women?

_____

_____

4. Summarizing Does the writer expect women to achieve their goals easily? Use information from the passage to support your answer.

_____

_____

✓ Applying the Skill

Directions: In each blank at the left, write the letter of the choice that best answers the question.

_____ **1.** To whom do the women of the United States have to appeal to get the rights they want?

    A. other American women   **C.** the men of the United States

    B. all women voters   **D.** both men and women who are married

_____ **2.** What would be the reason for publishing a document such as the Declaration of Sentiments?

    A. to show that women could write such a document

    B. to sue the men of the United States in court

    C. to bring public attention to the lack of women's rights

    D. to encourage women to form an independent nation

_____ **3.** Which of the following statements best describe the main sentiment of the woman who wrote this passage?

    A. pleased, but hoping for improvements

    B. unhappy, but hopeful about the future

    C. unhappy, but pessimistic about the future

    D. It is impossible to know her sentiments from reading this passage.

Geography and History Activity
The Age of Reform

Revival and Reform Across the Land

A New Kind of Religion

In the early 1800s, many Americans began to attend religious revivals, especially in the Northern part of the country. People would travel great distances to pray, sing, and shout, and to hear preachers like Charles Grandison Finney. Finney, and others like him, believed religion was something for men and women *to do*. This went against the religious teachings of the first Great Awakening in the 1700s, which said man was unable to save himself. The new religious activism stressed taking moral action against wrongdoing. By the 1820s, this belief had turned into a powerful spiritual movement called the Second Great Awakening. People from all religious denominations joined in. Men and women were inspired by the new call to action. They hoped to reform their own lives and American society.

Reforming the Nation

Lyman Beecher, a Connecticut minister, led a crusade to ban the use of alcohol. He and other reformers urged temperance—drinking little or no alcohol—in lectures and at rallies. In 1851 Maine became the first state to outlaw the sale and consumption of alcohol.

In the mid-1800s, most females and African Americans received little education. Schools were poorly funded, and teachers often lacked training. Horace Mann, a lawyer, led the fight for educational reforms. His state, Massachusetts, founded the nation's first state-supported normal school, which trained high school graduates to become teachers. Dozens of new colleges and universities sprang up around the country, though most admitted only men. In 1833 Oberlin College of Ohio was founded, welcoming women and African Americans.

Other reformers turned their attention to helping people with special needs. Dorothea Dix worked to improve conditions in institutions for the mentally ill and prisoners, as well as to educate the public about their plights. Thomas Gallaudet became an advocate for the hearing impaired, establishing the Hartford School for the Deaf in Connecticut in 1817. The visually impaired were suddenly able to "read" with their fingers when Samuel Gridley Howe developed books with large raised letters.

Writers and Artists Respond

The spiritual and social changes sweeping the country affected America's artists and writers. Transcendentalist writers like Ralph Waldo Emerson, Margaret Fuller, and Henry David Thoreau stressed listening to the inner voice of conscience. Fuller supported women's rights and Thoreau practiced civil disobedience when he refused to obey laws he believed were unjust.

The voice of conscience in America would soon lead to another social reform movement: the abolition of slavery.

Geography and History Activity (continued)

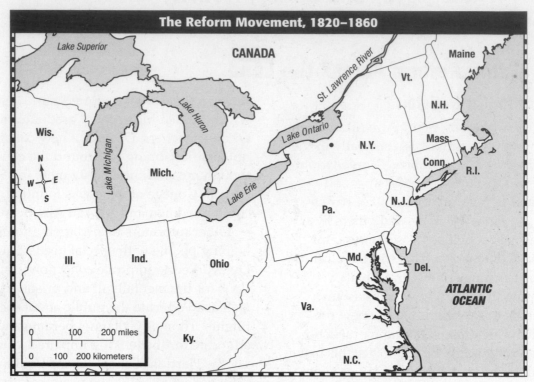

The Reform Movement, 1820–1860

Lake Superior

CANADA

St. Lawrence River

Maine

Vt.

N.H.

Lake Huron

Lake Ontario

Mass.

Wis.

N.Y.

Lake Michigan

Conn.

R.I.

Mich.

N
W   E
S

Lake Erie

N.J.

Pa.

Ill.

Ind.

Ohio

Md.

Del.

ATLANTIC
OCEAN

Va.

0   100   200 miles

Ky.

0   100   200 kilometers

N.C.

Directions: Write your answers to questions 1–5 on the map or in the spaces provided. You may draw lines and use abbreviations for your answers.

1. **Locating** Outline in red the state that was first to pass a law banning the manufacture and sale of alcoholic beverages. Write the name of the movement that urged the passage of such a law on or near this state.

2. **Identifying** Outline in blue the state that was first to reform American education. On or near the state, write the name of the man who led this reform.

3. **Contrasting** How did beliefs of the Second Great Awakening differ from the basic

teachings of the first Great Awakening in the 1700s?

_____

_____

4. **Labeling** Oberlin College was among the first to admit two groups of people who had often been denied college educations. Write the two groups the college admitted on the state where the college was located.

GOING FURTHER ▶ ▶▶▶

• Many groups of people, in search of an ideal society, established utopian communities in the eighteenth and nineteenth centuries. Conduct research on one of these communities for an oral

presentation. Where was it located? How successful was it, and why or why not? Who were its members? What was daily life like?

Linking Past and Present Activity

The Age of Reform

Public Education

THEN As of 1830, no state had a system of universal public education. During the colonial period, some New England towns established free schools supported by churches or private individuals, but they were overcrowded and lacked well-trained teachers. Wealthy families often hired tutors to teach their children. The poor usually did not educate their children at all.

By the mid-1800s, many of the nation's leaders demanded free public schools supported by taxes. An active leader in the movement was Horace Mann. In 1837 he reorganized the Massachusetts school system, lengthened the academic year to six months, increased teachers' salaries, enriched the curriculum, and founded the first teacher-training college in the United States.

Other states followed Massachusetts's lead. They prepared better textbooks and introduced new subjects, such as geography and history. By the 1850s, all states accepted the principle of tax-supported elementary schools. At the beginning of the Civil War, the United States had the highest literacy rate of any nation in the world.

NOW An important development in education since the 1850s is the effort to guarantee equal educational opportunities to all children. In the mid-1800s, the first public high schools were for males only. Today's public schools are open to boys and girls, and children of all races and ethnic backgrounds.

As public education became more available, the percentage of students completing high school and college increased steadily. In 1910 approximately 15 percent of adults over the age of 25 had completed four years of high school. In 1930 that number had risen to 20 percent, and it climbed to 33 percent by 1950. By 1970 approximately 56 percent of adults had completed high school, and in 1990, 77 percent had diplomas.

In 2000, 84 percent of adults had completed high school.

The percentage of college graduates has increased as well, but at a slower pace. From 1910 to 1960, the percentage grew from 5 percent to 10 percent. In 1990 the percentage of college graduates had grown another 11 percent, and by 2000 it stood at 26 percent.

High School Graduates and College Graduates in the U.S.

Percent of Adults (y-axis: 0, 10, 20, 30, 40, 50, 60, 70, 80, 90)

Years (x-axis: 1910, 1930, 1950, 1970, 1990)

Completing a Graph DIRECTIONS: Using the data provided in the text above, draw two lines on the graph—one showing the percentage of high school graduates and the other showing the percentage of college graduates from 1910 to 2000. Label each line. What might account for the increase in college graduates after 1970?

Copyright © Glencoe/McGraw-Hill, a division of The McGraw-Hill Companies, Inc.

Time Line Activity

The Age of Reform

Some Minority Milestones (1827–1871)

Directions: Complete the time line by entering the milestones for women
and African Americans in the appropriate spaces.

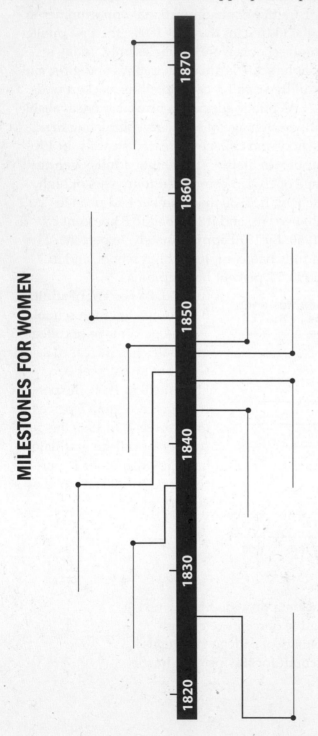

MILESTONES FOR WOMEN

MILESTONES FOR AFRICAN AMERICANS

Milestones for Women

- Mary Lyon founds Mount Holyoke Female Seminary in 1837.
- The first U. S. women's rights assembly meets in 1848 at Seneca Falls.
- In 1849 Elizabeth Blackwell is the first American woman to receive a medical diploma.
- Sofya Kovalevskaya, the first woman to be admitted into the prestigious Academy of Sciences, is born in Russia in 1850.
- Matilde Bajer founds a feminist library and discussion group in 1871 in Denmark.

Milestones for African Americans

- In 1827 Samuel Cornish and John Russwurm start the first African American newspaper.
- Sojourner Truth begins her reform mission in 1843.
- In 1845 Macon B. Allen becomes the first African American to be admitted to practice law in the United States.
- Frederick Douglass begins publishing the *North Star* newspaper in 1847.
- Harriet Tubman escapes from her slaveholders in 1849 and begins her work on the Underground Railroad.

School-to-Home Connection Activity
The Age of Reform

What Do You Know?

Directions: Ask each other the following questions to see how much you know about the social reforms of the early and mid-1800s.*

Student: What are utopias?

Partner's answer:

Student's answer:

Partner: What group stressed the relationship between humans and nature?

Student: Who wrote *American Slavery As It Is* in 1839?

Partner's answer:

Student's answer:

Partner: What was the most controversial issue at the Seneca Falls Convention?

*With your student, find answers to these questions in the student textbook.

School-to-Home Connection Activity (continued)

Understanding the Essential Questions

Directions: Rewrite each Essential Question as a statement. Then use your textbook to help you write details that support your statement in the graphic organizer provided.

Section 1 How did religion influence the social reforms in the United States during the early and mid-1800s?

Statement: _____

The Second Great Awakening inspired many people to believe that the nation's ideals of liberty and equality should be extended to all Americans. ⇨	**Response of Reformers**

Section 2 How did abolitionists influence the antislavery movement?

Statement: _____

Section 3 What were the effects of the women's rights movement of the middle to late 1800s?

Statement: _____

Education	Rights Within Marriage	Professions

Reteaching Activity
The Age of Reform

A spirit of reform swept the nation in the mid-1800s. Some reform leaders worked to improve education and prison conditions. Others hoped to extend the ideals of liberty and equality to all Americans by ending slavery and promoting rights for women. Reform efforts brought important changes to American society.

Identifying   DIRECTIONS: Each person listed below made important contributions to the reform movements of the 1800s. Write the names next to their contributions in the chart.

Dorothea Dix	**Harriet Tubman**	**Sarah and Angelina Grimké**
Elizabeth Blackwell	**Horace Mann**	**Susan B. Anthony**
Elizabeth Cady Stanton	**Lyman Beecher**	**Thomas Gallaudet**
Frederick Douglass	**Mary Lyon**	**William Lloyd Garrison**

Contributions	Reformer
1. after escaping from slavery, became a powerful voice for abolition in speaking engagements around the world	
2. became a successful doctor at a time when medicine was considered a male profession	
3. developed a method to educate people with hearing impairments	
4. called for equal pay for women and coeducation; founded the Daughters of Temperance	
5. brought attention to poor conditions for the mentally ill and prisoners	
6. insisted that the Declaration of Sentiments include a demand for woman suffrage	
7. pushed for improvements in education, leading to the nation's first state-supported schools	
8. established Mount Holyoke Female Seminary	
9. wrote *American Slavery As It Is*, firsthand accounts of life under slavery	
10. used lectures, pamphlets, and rallies to promote temperance	
11. famed African American conductor on the Underground Railroad	
12. founded *The Liberator* and the New England Anti-Slavery Society	

Copyright © Glencoe/McGraw-Hill, a division of The McGraw-Hill Companies, Inc.

Section Resources

Guided Reading Activity

The Age of Reform

Social Reform

Reading Tip Reading in short spurts helps you stay focused. Read for 30 minutes and take a break. Pick up where you left off for another 30 minutes and take another break.

Outlining **DIRECTIONS:** Read the section and complete the outline below.

I. Religion and Reform

   A. Religious revivals were one part of the wave of religious feeling called

   the _____.

   B. Communities called _____ wanted to create a perfect society.

   C. The _____ movement warned of the dangers of liquor.

   D. _____ schools trained high-school graduates to become teachers.

   E. _____ College was an unusual institution of higher education because it admitted women and African Americans.

   F. Thomas Gallaudet developed a method to educate people who

   were _____.

   G. _____ worked to improve poor conditions for prisoners and the mentally ill.

II. Cultural Trends

   A. _____ emphasized the relationship between humans and nature.

   B. Henry Thoreau practiced _____ when he went to jail rather than pay a tax.

   C. During the first half of the 1800s, the authors of the most popular

   works of fiction were _____.

   D. Harriet Beecher Stowe wrote the novel _____, which examined the injustice of slavery.

Copyright © Glencoe/McGraw-Hill, a division of The McGraw-Hill Companies, Inc.

Guided Reading Activity

The Age of Reform

The Abolitionists

Reading Tip

Take notes as you read the textbook. Then periodically review your notes. Reviewing your notes from time to time will prepare you for taking the test.

Filling in the Blanks   DIRECTIONS: Use your textbook to fill in the blanks using the words in the box. Some words may not be used.

Liberia	abolitionists	Frederick Douglass
Sojourner Truth	American Colonization Society	Ghana
The Liberator	Harriet Tubman	William Lloyd Garrison
Theodore Weld	Underground Railroad	Quaker
Africa	Grimké	Elijah Lovejoy

Reformers who worked to end slavery were called **(1)** _____. Many of their leaders came from the **(2)** _____ faith. An early effort to end slavery involved the **(3)** _____, which sent freed people to western **(4)** _____. Many settled there in the new country of **(5)** _____.

Abolitionists, however, realized that the slavery issue had to be addressed in the United States. New England's **(6)** _____ started antislavery societies and a newspaper called **(7)** _____. The **(8)** _____ sisters from South Carolina freed their own enslaved workers.

African American abolitionists included **(9)** _____, who was a powerful and influential speaker and newspaper editor, and Isabella Baumfree, who changed her name to **(10)** _____. Some African Americans who escaped from slavery were helped by abolitionists who ran the **(11)** _____ from the South to the North.

Opposition to abolitionism was sometimes violent. **(12)** _____ was killed defending his antislavery newspaper in Illinois.

Copyright © Glencoe/McGraw-Hill, a division of the McGraw-Hill Companies, Inc.

Guided Reading Activity

The Age of Reform

The Women's Movement

Reading Tip Set a goal for completing and understanding this reading assignment in less than one hour.

Reading for Accuracy **DIRECTIONS:** Use your textbook to decide if a statement is true or false. Write **T** or **F** in the blank. If a statement is false, rewrite it to make it true.

_____ **1.** Elizabeth Cady Stanton and Lucretia Mott helped organize the first women's rights convention in 1848.

_____

_____ **2.** The most controversial issue at the 1848 convention was slavery.

_____

_____ **3.** Male reformers such as Frederick Douglass supported the women's rights movement.

_____

_____ **4.** Susan B. Anthony led a movement against women's rights and temperance.

_____

_____ **5.** New York was the first state to grant women the right to vote.

_____

_____ **6.** Catherine Beecher and Emma Hart Willard believed women did not need to be educated because they held traditional female roles.

_____

_____ **7.** Women did make some gains in marriage, property, and divorce laws during the last half of the 1800s.

_____

_____ **8.** Many career choices were open to women during the 1800s.

_____

Copyright © Glencoe/McGraw-Hill, a division of The McGraw-Hill Companies, Inc.

Answer Key

Nationalism and Sectionalism

Citizenship and Decision-Making Activity

Questions to Consider
1. Student answers will vary but should display an understanding of the strong tie the Cherokee had to their native lands.
2. The Cherokee who escaped later formed part of the Eastern Band. Many of them live now on a reservation in North Carolina.

Your Task
Check students' Self-Assessment Checklists. Students should complete the Citizenship and Decision-Making Activity by working individually or in a group as directed in the How to Do It section. At the end of the project, have students review their work by discussing difficulties they may have faced during the project and how they resolved those difficulties. Encourage students to explain how they would improve their work if they did this project again.

Economics and History Activity

Applying Economics to History
1. The banks promised to exchange them for gold or silver on demand of the holder.
2. The banks often did not have enough gold and silver on hand to fulfill the promise to exchange the notes for gold or silver on demand. As a result, people did not trust the notes. This caused the notes to lose value.
3. Jackson's veto caused the National Bank to cease operations. As a result, the economy experienced wide fluctuations in the money supply. Without a central bank to set limits, state banks printed money and made loans as they saw fit. These changes in the money supply caused wide swings in economic activity.
4. The Fed uses its reserve requirement, among other tools, to influence the money supply to help stabilize the economy.
5. $Y = \$100,000 \times 0.15 = \$15,000$;
   $Z = \$100,000 - \$15,000 = \$85,000$

Going Further With Economics

Tool	Fed Action	Money Supply (increases or decreases)
Reserve Requirement	Lower	Increases
	Raise	Decreases
Open Market Operations	Buy bonds	Increases
	Sell bonds	Decreases
Discount Rate	Lower	Increases
	Raise	Decreases

Reading Skills Activity

Practicing the Skill
1. the founding of the Mormon church and the difficulties it faced in its early years
2. Mormons believed that property should be held in common and initially practiced polygamy.
3. Smith was killed by people who were angered by Mormon beliefs and practices.

As leader of the Mormons, he was a prime target for those who opposed their beliefs.

Applying the Skill
1. Mormons finally found a permanent home in the Great Salt Lake region, where they built large and prosperous communities.
2. Deseret was the name Mormons gave to the Great Salt Lake region.

Copyright © Glencoe/McGraw-Hill, a division of The McGraw-Hill Companies, Inc.

Answer Key

3. The Mormons migrated west in search of religious freedom; the forty-niners were searching for gold.

4. Living conditions were harsh. The region the Mormons settled was a desert, which they made habitable only through "hard work and determination." They had to build irrigation canals to water their farms.

5. The Mormon migration came first, in 1846. When the forty-niners passed through Utah on their way to California, the Mormons were already there to sell them supplies.

6. Utah was settled largely by Mormons, whose beliefs were quite different from∞those of most other Americans. Many people distrusted the Mormons. Also, Mormons wished to be self-sufficient and possibly resented interference by the U.S. government into their affairs.

American Literature Reading

1. The writer was friendly with the white leader of the fort and often helped supply food for the soldiers there.

2. The braves traveled across the prairie to reach better hunting grounds to provide deer for the fort at Peoria.

3. The writer understood that some white people were honest, trustworthy, and good friends (like the head of the fort at Peoria) and some were cruel and unjust (like the white men who murdered most of the hunting party). Despite the writer's great loss, he did not hold the leader of the fort responsible for the cruelty of other whites toward Native Americans.

Interpreting Political Cartoons

1. The judge is pictured seated on bales of cotton and tobacco because these were the important crops of Southern agriculture and the foundation of the South's economy. The labor force on cotton and tobacco plantations was comprised mainly of enslaved African Americans. The judge is protecting the South's economy by denouncing antislavery activity.

2. The judge has his foot on the Constitution to show that he is ignoring the argument in the Declaration of Independence that all people should be born free and treated equally.

3. The donkey's ears and the whip are further criticisms of the judge. The ears are meant to show that the judge is stubborn, and the whip stands for slavery and its cruelties.

4. Southerners would not have wanted abolitionists in the South because the success of the Southern economy depended on slave labor. Abolitionists might lead to uprisings and rebellions against the institution of slavery.

5. The title "Southern Ideas of Liberty" is a further criticism of slavery in the South and the mistreatment of white activists working against slavery in the South.

6. By portraying the South as cruel and stubborn, the cartoon is clearly more sympathetic to abolitionists.

The Jackson Era

Content Vocabulary Activity

1. relocate
2. plurality
3. veto
4. guerrilla tactics
5. spoils system
6. tariff
7. depression
8. secede
9. majority
10. caucus
11. laissez-faire
12. nominating convention
13. nullify

Copyright © Glencoe/McGraw-Hill, a division of The McGraw-Hill Companies, Inc.

Answer Key

Academic Vocabulary Activity

A. Word Meaning
1. discard
2. sit out
3. regional
4. perish
5. store
6. currency

B. Word Usage
1. survived
2. symbols
3. selection
4. institution
5. federal

C. Word Family
1. verb, adjective
2. noun
3. verb, adjective
4. noun
5. verb
6. adjective
7. noun
8. verb
9. verb, adjective
10. noun
11. noun
12. verb
13. noun
14. verb
15. adjective

Primary Source Readings
1. Burnett had hunted with the Cherokee and slept in their camps.
2. Answers will vary. Imagery includes "arrested and dragged," "driven at the bayonet point into the stockades," "chill of a drizzling rain," "loaded like cattle or sheep," and "the sadness and solemnity."
3. Burnett blames many deaths on the disease pneumonia.
4. Burnett was correct. In time, Americans viewed the government's treatment of the Cherokee as shameful and wrong.
5. Answers will vary and should reflect the students' knowledge of the passage.

Writing Skills Activity

Practicing the Skill
1. C
2. E
3. D
4. A
5. B

Applying the Skill
Check students' Self-Assessment Checklists. Students' descriptions should include detailed and vivid descriptions of the White House reception as well as creative word choices. They should check their work for correct spelling, grammar, and punctuation.

Social Studies Skills Activity

Practicing the Skill
5. Jackson refuses to sign a new Bank charter in 1836 and it closes.
3. Jackson's veto is supported, resulting in his reelection.
1. Clay and Webster persuade Biddle to apply for a new Bank charter.
2. Jackson rejects the charter application by veto.
4. Jackson withdraws all government deposits from the Bank.

Applying the Skill
Answers will vary. Students create their own sequence of events time line.

Differentiated Instruction Activity
1. The northern route started near the North Carolina-Tennessee border and crossed central Tennessee, southwestern Kentucky, and southern Illinois. After crossing the Mississippi River north of Cape Girardeau, Missouri, the route moved across southern Missouri and the northwest corner of Arkansas before entering Indian Territory.
2. Distances: Water Route—approximately 900 miles; Northern Route—approximately 700 miles; Benge's Route—approximately 600 miles; Bell's Route—approximately 600 miles. Students' estimates of the journey lengths will vary but should realistically consider how far the Cherokee could have traveled each day by land or water. Students' speculations should take into account that the longer the journey was, the

Copyright © Glencoe/McGraw-Hill, a division of The McGraw-Hill Companies, Inc.

Answer Key

greater the risk of the Cherokee dying of disease, starvation, or exposure before arriving at their destination.

Critical Thinking Skills Activity

Practicing the Skill

1. Although many people are upset about the treatment of Native Americans and their removal from their lands, it is a positive development because white settlers have improved the lands.

2. He sees them as savages.

3. He argues that removal of the Native Americans is one more betrayal in a long series of betrayals by the U.S. government that have deprived Native Americans of millions of acres of land.

4. He sees Native Americans as victims of racism and unfair treatment who have suffered much at the hands of American settlers.

Applying the Skill

1. C   2. C   3. B

Geography and History Activity

1. Jackson was suspicious of the power of a national bank. He sought to destroy it by vetoing the renewal of its charter and withdrawing federal money from it. The national bank represented federalism, which he also distrusted.

2. Vermont, Massachusetts, Rhode Island, and Connecticut

3. Answers will vary but should mention that states east of the Appalachians were established for a longer time and, for the most part, had larger populations. Before 1832, it would be natural for successful presidential candidates to come from these states.

4. No. Even with these additional six states, Jackson would have had more electoral votes.

5. National Republicans favored a strong central government, so they probably were not afraid of the National Bank becoming too powerful.

Linking Past and Present Activity

1. C   4. A
2. D   5. F
3. E   6. B

Time Line Activity

1. Jackson first ran for the presidency in 1824. Jackson won the popular vote plurality, but Adams was named president.

2. two

3. States eliminated the property ownership requirement for voting.

4. They allowed the people to choose presidential electors.

School-to-Home Connection Activity

What Do You Know?

Sample answers:

Partner's answer: Favorite sons are political candidates who are backed by their home states rather than the national party.

Student's answer: The "Five Civilized Tribes" originally lived in Georgia, Alabama, Mississippi, and Florida.

Partner's answer: Osceola was the Seminole chief who defended his tribe's lands in Florida from settlers and soldiers.

Student's answer: Laissez-faire is the principle that the government should interfere as little as possible in the nation's economy.

Copyright © Glencoe/McGraw-Hill, a division of The McGraw-Hill Companies, Inc.

Answer Key

Understanding the Essential Questions

Sample answers:

1. Statement: Political beliefs and events shaped Andrew Jackson's presidency:

Political Beliefs and Events	Effect on Jackson's Presidency
Jackson declared "equal protection and equal benefits" for all white American men.	For the first time, white male sharecroppers, factory workers, and others participated in the political process.
Democrats wanted to open up government jobs to people from all walks of life.	President Jackson fired federal workers and replaced them with his supporters. This practice became known as the spoils system.
Jackson's supporters stopped using the caucus system in which members of Congress chose major candidates.	Caucuses were replaced by nominating conventions. These allowed many people to participate in the selection of candidates.

2. Statement: Native Americans suffered losses during Andrew Jackson's presidency.

Attitude or Event	How It Affected Native Americans
Jackson's frontier background led him to support the settlers' demand for Native American land and push the Indian Removal Act through Congress.	The Indian Removal Act allowed the federal government to pay Native Americans to move west. Most Native American leaders felt forced to accept payment for their lands.
Jackson supported Georgia's efforts to remove the Cherokee, and the federal government persuaded some Cherokee to sign The Treaty of New Echota.	The Cherokee refused to honor the treaty but were forced to leave their homes in Georgia and walk to Oklahoma. This became known as the Trail of Tears.

3. How do economic issues affect the president and presidential elections?

Effects on the President	Effects on Presidential Elections
The president's actions can affect economic property.	The national economic situation can swap the elections from the one party to another.
People can blame the president for economic downturn even if it was caused by other means.	A president's economic policies can win favor or opposion with the public.

Reteaching Activity

Democracy: nominating conventions, spoils system, suffrage expanded

View: Equality; broader participation in politics and government

Tariff Debate: Nullification Act, secession threat, Force Bill

View: supported Union over states' rights

Native Americans: Indian Removal Act, *Worcester* v. *Georgia*, Trail of Tears, Dade Massacre

View: favored settlers' demands over Native American rights

Bank of the United States: veto of charter bill, government deposits withdrawn

View: Bank benefited wealthy Easterners, not ordinary citizens; unconstitutional

Guided Reading Activity

Jacksonian Democracy

1. F. Andrew Jackson won a plurality but not the majority of electoral votes.

131

Answer Key

2. T.
3. F. The National Republicans supported a strong central government and federal measures to shape the nation's economy.
4. T.
5. F. The practice of replacing government employees with an election winner's supporters is known as the spoils system.
6. T.
7. T.

Conflicts Over Land

I. A. Five Civilized
   B. Indian Removal
   C. Indian Territory
   D. John Marshall
   E. Trail of Tears
II. A. Illinois
   B. Seminole
   C. Osceola
   D. reservations; tribes

Jackson and the Bank

1. Bank of the United States
2. Henry Clay
3. veto
4. Martin Van Buren
5. Whigs
6. depression
7. treasury
8. laissez-faire
9. William Henry Harrison
10. John Tyler
11. sectional
12. James Polk

Manifest Destiny

Content Vocabulary Activity

1. joint occupation
2. mountain men
3. rendezvous
4. emigrants
5. prairie schooners
6. Manifest Destiny
7. Tejanos
8. empresario
9. decree
10. annex
11. Californios
12. rancho
13. ranchero
14. ceded
15. forty-niners
16. boomtown
17. vigilante

Academic Vocabulary Activity

A. Word Meaning

1. ability to get to
2. source of wealth
3. set up
4. take away
5. begin
6. fundamental laws
7. include

B. Word Family

1. verb
2. adjective
3. noun, verb
4. noun
5. adjective
6. verb
7. noun
8. verb, adjective
9. verb
10. noun
11. verb
12. noun
13. verb

Primary Source Readings

1. The guards began to build a cabin.
2. Moses is worried and anxious about the other members of the group who went on ahead.
3. Moses's spirits rise when he finds some steel traps so that he can have meat to eat.
4. Moses reads aloud in order to break the silence.

Answer Key

5. Answers will vary and can include responses such as loneliness, fear of starvation, and worry or anxiety.

Writing Skills Activity

Practicing the Skill
The sequence of activities is 4, 1, 2, 5, 7, 6, 3.

Applying the Skill
Check students' Self-Assessment Checklists. The sequence of the given activities is listed below. The additional steps from the students should be placed in their proper order.

1. Purchase prairie schooner.

2. Pack wagon with supplies.

3. Load wagon onto steamship at St. Louis for upstream journey.

4. Organize traveling party for overland journey after disembarking in Independence.

5. Make camp for night at Shawnee Mission, Kansas.

6. Sell excess goods at Ft. Laramie, Wyoming.

Social Studies Skills Activity

Practicing the Skill
1. The time span is 1815 to 1840. The time intervals are 5 years.

2. 1821

3. 23 days—April 21 to May 14

4. after

Applying the Skill
1. The four items should be added to the time line in the appropriate boxes.

2. The time span is January 1846 to May 1848. The time intervals are four months.

3. The three states are California, Texas, and New Mexico. New Mexico was secured first, in August 1846.

Differentiated Instruction Activity
1. James Marshall took the following steps to verify that his discovery was gold: (1) Beat it into a different shape to test its malleability; (2) allowed P.L. Wimmer's wife to boil it in lye and saleratus; (3) directed Mr. Bennett to beat it very thin; (4) tested it with nitric acid; (5) compared its weight with three silver dollars.

2. Students should recognize the economic principles of supply and demand at work. Resources were scarce and therefore valuable; miners often had a considerable amount of disposable income.

Critical Thinking Skills Activity

Practicing the Skill
1. Students should predict that the joint occupation would lead to conflict because either the United States or Britain eventually would seek full control of the area.

2. Students should predict that the Americans eventually would gain control of the area because of their greater population numbers.

3. Oregon was located adjacent to the United States, making the annexation of Oregon a goal for Americans. But because the British shared the territory, it became a source of direct conflict and possible confrontation between the United States and Britian.

4. Student's answers will vary but should include an understanding of the population changes on Oregon. People will pass trough Oregon, creating business opportunities. Some people will stay in Oregon, while others will move on to California.

Applying the Skill
1. B   **2.** C   **3.** D

Geography and History Activity
1. New Mexico, California, Texas, Colorado, Arizona, Utah, Wyoming, Kansas, and Oklahoma

Answer Key

2. The climate was dry, and the vegetation was similar. The Spanish brought animals and plants that could adapt to dry environments.

3. The Spanish taught them to herd animals like cattle on horseback, a good skill to have for the open-range style of ranching.

4. They had good survival instincts and could adapt to any environment.

5. Answers may include that the Spanish introduced animals, like cattle and horses, and plants and farming methods to the Southwest. Open-range ranching became a way of life all over the Southwest and a big part of American culture.

Linking Past and Present Activity

Students' lists will vary but might include tools (ax, shovel, hoe), food supplies (flour, sugar, lard, dried meat, fruit), cooking utensils (kettles, silverware), blankets, lanterns, clothing, and seeds for planting. Students should explain why it would be necessary to bring the items they have chosen.

Time Line Activity

Texas

1821	Americans invited to Texas
1830	Mexico stops U.S. immigration
1833	Santa Anna becomes dictator
1836	Texas declares independence
1836	Houston defeats Santa Anna
1845	Texas is admitted as a state

Understanding the Essential Questions

Sample answers:
1. Statement: The idea of Manifest Destiny influenced western settlement.

The United States was destined to extend its boundaries to the Pacific.	Therefore →	Americans believed it was their right to possess the whole continent, even if it meant taking land from other people.

California

1821	California becomes a state of Mexico
1839	Sutter builds trading post
1845	Polk offers to purchase California
1846	Mexican War
1846	Bear Flag Republic is proclaimed
1850	California is admitted as a state

School-to-Home Connection Activity

What Do You Know?

Sample answers:

Partner's answer: "Fifty-Four Forty or Fight" referred to the line of latitude that the Democrats believed should be the nation's northern border in Oregon.

Student's answer: Texas colonists agreed to learn Spanish, become Mexican citizens, convert to Catholicism, and obey Mexican law.

Partner's answer: William Becknell was the first American trader to reach the Mexican settlement of Santa Fe. His travel route came to be known as the Santa Fe Trail.

Student's answer: California's constitution banned slavery, and the Southern states were concerned that making California a state would upset the balance of free and slave states.

Answer Key

2. Statement: Texans fought for their independence from Mexico.

Mexican government: stopped all immigration from the U.S.; encouraged immigration of Mexicans and Europeans; taxed U.S. imports; planned to end slavery; General Santa Anna named himself dictator and overthrew Mexico's constitution.	
Texan settlers: demanded that American settlers be allowed to immigrate into Texas; demanded that Texas become a separate Mexican state; felt betrayed by the Mexican government; had small, violent rebellions before the fight began.	

⟹ The fight begins for the independence of Texas.

3. Mexican lands in the West became part of the United States through several means.

Event	How the Land Became Part of the United States
Treaty of Guadalupe Hidalgo	Mexico gave up all claims to Texas and agreed to the Rio Grande as the border between Texas and Mexico.
Mexican Cession	Mexico sold its provinces of California and New Mexico to the United States for the price of $15 million.
Gadsden Purchase	The United States paid Mexico $10 million for a strip of land along the southern edge of present-day Arizona and New Mexico.

4. Statement: Many factors affected the settlement of California and Utah.

California	Utah
Gold was discovered in 1848.	Settled by Mormons trying to escape persecution and find religious freedom

Reteaching Activity

1. T	**6.** U	**11.** O	**16.** CN, U
2. CN	**7.** O	**12.** U	**17.** T
3. CN	**8.** U	**13.** O	
4. T	**9.** T	**14.** T	
5. CN	**10.** CN	**15.** O	

Texas: 14, 1, 9, 17, 4

Oregon: 7, 11, 15, 13

Utah: 8, 12, 6, 16

California & New Mexico: 2, 10, 5, 3, 16

Guided Reading Activity

The Oregon Country

1. The United States, Great Britain, Spain, and Russia claimed the Oregon Country.

2. Spain agreed to set the limits of its territory at what is now California's northern border and to give up its claims to Oregon.

3. The rendezvous of mountain men was the annual gathering in which they met with trading companies and with each other for business and relaxation.

4. The Whitmans were missionaries who went to Oregon and built a mission among the Cayuse people.

5. Emigrants were pioneers who left the United States to settle in Oregon.

6. People first thought that the country should be a model of freedom and democracy. That vision changed to the belief that the United States should spread freedom by occupying the entire continent.

7. John O'Sullivan called this idea Manifest Destiny.

8. The slogan referred to the line of latitude that should be the nation's northern border in Oregon.

Answer Key

Independence for Texas

I.
- **A.** Tejanos
- **B.** Empresarios
- **C.** Stephen Austin
- **D.** tax
- **E.** Santa Anna

II.
- **A.** Alamo
- **B.** republic
- **C.** Sam Houston
- **D.** Goliad
- **E.** San Jacinto
- **F.** annex
- **G.** James Polk

War With Mexico

1. New Mexico
2. Santa Fe Trail
3. California
4. ranchos
5. James K. Polk
6. Zachary Taylor
7. Stephen Watts Kearny
8. John C. Frémont
9. Californios
10. Bear Flag
11. Mexico City
12. Guadalupe Hidalgo
13. Rio Grande
14. Mexican Cession

California and Utah

1. F. People who arrived in California in 1849 to seek gold were called forty-niners.
2. T.
3. F. Most miners found little or no gold.
4. T.
5. F. California's constitution banned slavery.
6. F. The founder of the Mormon Church was Joseph Smith.
7. T.
8. T.

North and South

Content Vocabulary Activity

1. capital
2. strike
3. tenant farmer
4. Morse code
5. discrimination
6. spiritual
7. clipper ship
8. famine
9. yeoman
10. cotton gin
11. overseer
12. telegraph
13. nativist
14. literacy
15. trade union
16. slave codes
17. prejudice

Academic Vocabulary Activity

A. Word Meaning

1. E
2. C
3. F
4. A
5. D
6. B

B. Word Usage

1. A   2. C   3. B

Primary Source Readings

1. The author believes that the general public has a low view of African Americans.
2. Death would be no change in the way the author is living now.
3. The author stops writing because he cannot bear to write any more. He is full of despair; there is no point in writing more.
4. The author puts "Christian" in italics because African Americans are treated in an un-Christian manner.
5. Responses will vary.

Answer Key

Writing Skills Activity

Practicing the Skill

Answers will vary. Students should list three statements/questions they will need to address. Sample answer:

1. Children are needed at home to help on the farm.
2. How are the children supposed to get to the school?
3. Education should be done privately. I don't want my taxes paying to educate others' children.

Applying the Skill

See students' Self-Assessment Checklist. Answers will vary, but students should choose an argument and then respond to it. For example, students may list an argument that enslaved workers should be taught to read and write. They may respond that literate slaves might lead others in rebellion.

Social Studies Skills Activity

Practicing the Skill

Students' tables will vary but should include the following:

Textile—Clothing

Metal—Watches, guns

Machinery—Agricultural machinery, sewing machines

Leather—Shoes

Students' tables will contain different entries for how each item produced was used.

Applying the Skill

1. Distribution of female American workers during 2006
2. 13,400,000; 20%
3. Students should refer to the table they completed for Practicing the Skill. They should contrast the information to the industries that women are working in today, using a well-composed paragraph.

Answers will vary but should specifically note the greater variety of jobs women have today.

Differentiated Instruction Activity

1. Items such as nuts, wood, corn shucks, cane, vines, apples, and gourds were used to make toys.
2. Sunday is the day of worship for Christians. Many devout Christians of the Old South refrained from work and all secular pursuits on Sunday and required their children to do the same.

Critical Thinking Skills Activity

Practicing the Skill

1. He was a slave as a child, but he was freed with his mother at the age of seven or eight. He is telling his story at the age of 80, so he was free most of his life.
2. He probably got it from his owner, whose last name was Holbert.
3. Several male members of the family left to serve in the war and never returned, so the war broke up his family. But the war also gave Clayton, his mother, his brother, and his sister their freedom.
4. It had a destructive effect on Clayton's family. His grandmother and mother continued in slavery long after they were freed because of dishonest slave traders, and this resulted in Clayton being born an enslaved person. His family was also broken up by slavery when his grandmother was sold to someone in Texas and they never saw her again.

Applying the Skill

1. B   2. C   3. A

Answer Key

Geography and History Activity

1. Pawtucket Falls was the key natural feature that attracted investors to the Lowell site.

2. The Lowell mills had access to the Merrimack River, the Concord River, Massachusetts Bay, and the Atlantic Ocean.

3. Lowell mill owners built six miles of canals, dammed the Merrimack River, and stored water in New Hampshire lakes to be released during dry seasons.

4. Answers will vary, but should mention disruption of the natural habitat including plants, fisheries, and animal habitats.

5. Raw material, cotton, was transported by sea from the South. It came through Newburyport near the mouth of the Merrimack River and up the river to Lowell.

Linking Past and Present Activity

1. The farm machines introduced in the 1830s substituted animal power for manual labor.

2. The divider on the McCormick reaper separated and cut standing grain.

3. If no one had invented the reaper, most farmers in the late nineteenth century probably would have worked small plots. They would have relied on manual labor to grow crops and would have been able to produce only enough to support their families.

4. The combine harvester was probably given that name because it combined the operations performed by the reaper and the thresher.

5. Manufacturers often describe engines in terms of horsepower to explain that the vehicle powered by that engine can do the work of a certain number of horses.

Time Line Activity

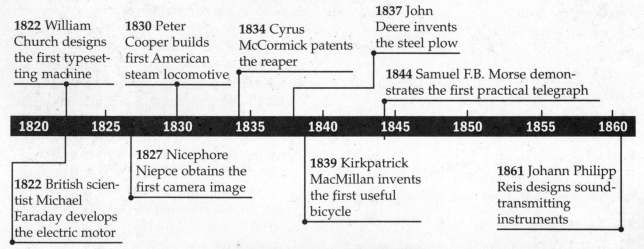

INVENTIONS IN AMERICA

1822 William Church designs the first typesetting machine

1830 Peter Cooper builds first American steam locomotive

1834 Cyrus McCormick patents the reaper

1837 John Deere invents the steel plow

1844 Samuel F.B. Morse demonstrates the first practical telegraph

1820   1825   1830   1835   1840   1845   1850   1855   1860

1822 British scientist Michael Faraday develops the electric motor

1827 Nicephore Niepce obtains the first camera image

1839 Kirkpatrick MacMillan invents the first useful bicycle

1861 Johann Philipp Reis designs sound-transmitting instruments

INVENTIONS ELSEWHERE

Answer Key

School-to-Home Connection Activity

What Do You Know?

Sample answers:

Partner's answer: They were called clippers because they "clipped" time from long journeys.

Student's answer: The striking workers wanted higher wages and to limit their work-day to 10 hours.

Partner's answer: The cotton gin enabled workers to clean 50 times more cotton per day. Because the cotton gin processed cotton so quickly, farmers wanted to grow more cotton to increase their profits.

Student's answer: White Southerners thought that enslaved people who could not read and write would be less likely to rebel.

Understanding the Essential Questions

Sample answers:

1. Statement: Several innovations in industry, travel, and communications changed the lives of Americans in the 1800s.

Innovations in Industry	Innovations in Travel	Innovations in Communications
• divided tasks among workers • built factories to make products more quickly • used steam- and water-powered machines • mass-produced goods • invention of the steel-tipped plow made planting easier • invention of the mechanical reaper sped up harvesting	• built thousands of miles of roads • built wider and deeper canals that opened new shipping routes • developed steamboats and clipper ships, which improved river and sea travel • built thousands of miles of rail-roads, connecting more cities • introduced the first steam-powered locomotive	• invention of the telegraph allowed people to communi-cate over great distances

2. Statement: Immigration had an impact on cities, industry, and culture in the North.

Immigration Impact	⟹	On cities: contributed to the significant increase in population
		On industry: provided cheap labor for the manufacturing industry
		On culture: brought their customs, religion, languages, food, and ways of life with them, which became part of American culture

3. Statement: The South's industry and economy differed from the industry and economy of the North.

	Type of Economy	Type of Labor	Rate of Industrial Growth
South	agricultural	relied on slave labor to produce crops	slow
North	industrial	relied on factory workers, including immigrants and children, to produce goods	rapid

Answer Key

4. Statement: Unique elements of culture developed among enslaved African Americans in the South.

Enslaved people knew their families could be separated, so they developed large, close-knit extended families that would care for each other.	Native-born African Americans held onto their African customs and passed them along to their children.	Many enslaved African Americans accepted Christianity, but often followed the religious beliefs and practices of their African ancestors as well.

Reteaching Activity

Answers that can be in any order are grouped below.

1 and 2. railroads, steamboats

3. lower prices

4. cotton gin

5 and 6. economy based on agriculture, reliance on slave labor

7 and 8. worker specialization, growth of factories

9. immigration

10. nativism

11. unions

12. slave codes

Guided Reading Activity

The North's Economy

1. First, manufacturers made products by dividing tasks among workers. Second, manufacturers built factories to bring specialized workers together. Third, factory workers used machinery to perform some of their work.

2. Elias Howe invented the sewing machine, which increased mass production of cotton textiles.

3. Peter Cooper designed and built the *Tom Thumb* steam locomotive.

4. Goods moved faster and more cheaply from the Midwest to the East. More people moved to the Midwest and developed towns and industries.

5. Morse code is a series of dots and dashes representing letters of the alphabet. It is used for transmitting messages by telegraph.

6. The three inventions were the steel-tipped plow, the mechanical reaper, and the thresher.

7. Because farmers could harvest wheat more quickly by using the reaper, they planted more wheat. Growing wheat became profitable and remained the Midwest's main economic activity.

The North's People

1. trade unions

2. strikes

3. wages

4. working hours

5. prejudice [or discrimination]

6. discrimination [or prejudice]

7. Sarah G. Bagley

8. Irish

9. famine

10. Germany

11. Nativists

12. Know-Nothing

Southern Cotton Kingdom

I. **A.** slavery
   B. cotton gin
   C. Upper; Deep
   D. enslaved people

II. **A.** capital
    B. North
    C. Tredegar Iron Works
    D. waterways
    E. railroads

Answer Key

The South's People
1. F. Most white Southerners were either small farmers without enslaved people or planters with only a few enslaved workers.
2. F. Most yeomen owned land and worked it themselves.
3. T.
4. F. Wives of plantation owners were in charge of their households; overseers supervised the field hands.
5. T.
6. F. Slavery remained legal in the South, but no new enslaved people could enter the United States.
7. T.
8. T.

The Age of Reform

Content Vocabulary Activity
1. normal school
2. Underground Railroad
3. coeducation
4. revival
5. civil disobedience
6. suffrage
7. utopia
8. abolitionist
9. temperance
10. transcendentalists

Academic Vocabulary Activity

A. Word Meaning
1. S
2. S
3. S
4. A
5. S

B. Word Usage
1. capable
2. medical
3. lecture
4. ministry
5. route

C. Word Family
1. noun, adjective
2. verb
3. noun, verb
4. verb, adjective
5. adjective
6. noun
7. noun
8. adjective
9. noun
10. noun, verb
11. noun

Primary Source Readings
1. Jones believes the correct term is *Woman's Wrongs.*
2. Jones says the point is that enslaved African Americans are human beings.
3. Jones blames women themselves for their condition.
4. Answers will vary. Some women need men's protection. Some women have not acted as rational and accountable people. Some women do not take responsibility for their own lives.
5. Answers will vary. The long practice of keeping power away from women prevents them from seeing that their lives lack justice and equal rights.

Writing Skills Activity

Practicing the Skill
1. The convention was called to help women achieve "Right, Truth, and Reason" and gain the right to vote.
2. Yes; she states, "Don't be discouraged at the probability of difficulties. Remember that contest with difficulty gives strength."
3. The tone is forceful and matter-of-fact.
4. Answers will vary.

Answer Key

Applying the Skills

Check students' Self-Assessment Checklists. Answers will vary but should focus on people who have used nonviolence to change laws. Students will likely list historical figures such as Mohandas Gandhi and Dr. Martin Luther King, Jr., but they may list others who have followed nonviolence principles.

Social Studies Skills Activity

Practicing the Skill

Center circle: Transcendentalists

1. The web diagram is about the transcendentalists during the Second Great Awakening.

2. Students should mention Emily Dickinson, Walt Whitman, or Henry Wadsworth Longfellow and the titles of their poems.

3. Margaret Fuller was a leader for women's rights.

4. Students should give their opinions as to whether or not the transcendental movement made a difference during the Second Great Awakening, and then support their answer.

Applying the Skill

Students create their own web organizer based upon a significant event that took place in their lives. Paragraphs are written about the main idea of the diagram and its details. Diagrams and paragraphs will vary.

Differentiated Instruction Activity

1. Students' answers will vary but should draw upon knowledge of the relationship between men and women as compared to the roles indicated in the reading.

2. Students' answers will vary. Possible answers: Carey may have supported women's right to vote because he advises husbands to view their wives as equals, to treat them with respect, and to seek their opinions and counsel on important matters. Carey may not have supported women's right to vote because, while he believes they should be treated with respect, he seems to have supported society's view that a woman's role was in her home.

Critical Thinking Skills Activity

Practicing the Skill

1. Answers may include the idea that some American women felt oppressed and angry because they were denied rights as the result of unjust laws and rules made by men.

2. There are a limited number of work opportunities for women, and women are paid very little for the jobs they are allowed to hold. Women are also denied admission to college, which limits their education and professional options.

Applying the Skill

1. C   4. C
2. C   5. B
3. B

Geography and History Activity

1. Maine should be outlined in red; temperance movement

2. Massachusetts should be colored in blue; Horace Mann.

Answer Key

3. Preachers from the 1700s believed man was unable to save himself. Preachers in the Second Great Awakening believed men and women help themselves by taking action against moral wrongdoing.

4. *Women* and *African Americans* should be written on the state of Ohio.

Linking Past and Present Activity

Students may answer that there were more college graduates after 1970 because baby boomers were entering college in those years. Also colleges were opening their doors to more women and minorities.

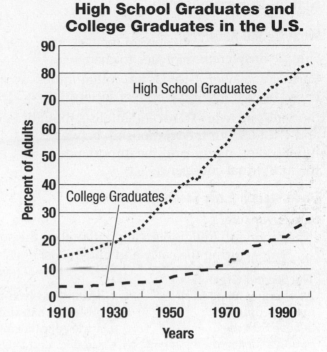

High School Graduates and College Graduates in the U.S.

Time Line Activity

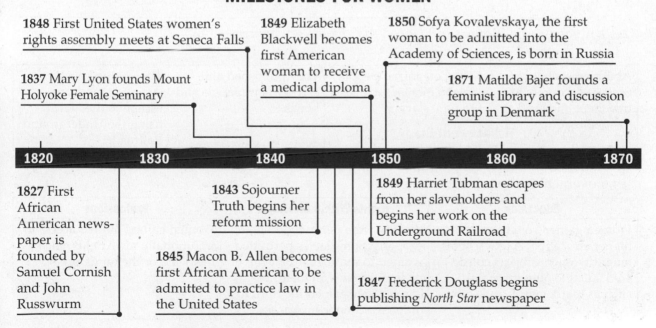

MILESTONES FOR WOMEN

1848 First United States women's rights assembly meets at Seneca Falls

1849 Elizabeth Blackwell becomes first American woman to receive a medical diploma

1850 Sofya Kovalevskaya, the first woman to be admitted into the Academy of Sciences, is born in Russia

1837 Mary Lyon founds Mount Holyoke Female Seminary

1871 Matilde Bajer founds a feminist library and discussion group in Denmark

| 1820 | 1830 | 1840 | 1850 | 1860 | 1870 |

1827 First African American newspaper is founded by Samuel Cornish and John Russwurm

1843 Sojourner Truth begins her reform mission

1849 Harriet Tubman escapes from her slaveholders and begins her work on the Underground Railroad

1845 Macon B. Allen becomes first African American to be admitted to practice law in the United States

1847 Frederick Douglass begins publishing *North Star* newspaper

MILESTONES FOR AFRICAN AMERICANS

Answer Key

School-to-Home Activity

What Do You Know?

Sample answers:

Partner's answer: Utopias are communities based on visions of the perfect society.

Student's answer: Transcendentalists thought and wrote about the relationship between humans and nature and the importance of the individual conscience.

Partner's answer: Sarah and Angelina Grimké, two sisters from a slaveholding family, and Angelina's husband, Theodore Weld wrote *American Slavery As It Is.*

Student's answer: The most controversial issue at the Seneca Falls Convention was women's suffrage, or whether women should have the right to vote.

Understanding the Essential Questions

Sample answers:

1. Statement: Religion greatly influenced the social reforms in the United States during the early and mid-1800s.

The Second Great Awakening inspired many people to believe that the nation's ideals of liberty and equality should be extended to all Americans.	**Response of Reformers** • became involved with social reform and missionary work • pushed to ban alcohol • made educational improvements • cared for and taught people with disabilities • educated the public on poor conditions for prisoners and the mentally ill • fought slavery • wrote literature that reflected American individualism and idealism

2. Statement: Abolitionists influenced the antislavery movement in several ways.

Abolitionists bought enslaved workers to free them and send them abroad.	They organized people in abolitionist societies to fight slavery.	They published anti-slavery newspapers and books.	They helped enslaved African Americans escape to the North using the Underground Railroad.

3. Statement: Women gained rights during the women's rights movement of the middle to late 1800s.

Education	Rights Within Marriage	Professions
Women gained some access to higher education. A few schools taught women subjects considered suitable only for males, such as mathematics and science.	Women were permitted to own property. Some states permitted women to share guardianship of their children with their husbands. They gained the right to divorce alcoholic husbands.	Women gained limited access to traditionally male fields, such as medicine or the ministry.

Answer Key

Reteaching Activity
1. Frederick Douglass
2. Elizabeth Blackwell
3. Thomas Gallaudet
4. Susan B. Anthony
5. Dorothea Dix
6. Elizabeth Cady Stanton
7. Horace Mann
8. Mary Lyon
9. Sarah and Angelina Grimké
10. Lyman Beecher
11. Harriet Tubman
12. William Lloyd Garrison

Guided Reading Activity

Social Reform
I. A. Second Great Awakening
   B. utopias
   C. temperance
   D. Normal
   E. Oberlin
   F. hearing impaired
   G. Dorothea Dix
II. A. Transcendentalists
   B. civil disobedience
   C. women
   D. *Uncle Tom's Cabin*

The Abolitionists
1. abolitionists
2. Quaker
3. American Colonization Society
4. Africa
5. Liberia
6. William Lloyd Garrison
7. *The Liberator*
8. Grimké
9. Frederick Douglass

10. Sojourner Truth
11. Underground Railroad
12. Elijah Lovejoy

The Women's Movement
1. T.
2. F. Suffrage was the most controversial issue at the 1848 convention.
3. T.
4. F. Susan B. Anthony worked for women's rights and temperance.
5. F. Wyoming was the first state that granted women the right to vote.
6. F. Catherine Beecher and Emma Hart Willard believed women should be educated for their traditional roles in life.
7. T.
8. F. Women had few career choices in the 1800s.